The ANTIQUE DOLLS DOLLHOUSES AND TOYS

Of the LEGO™ Foundation of Denmark

By Florence Theriault

Gold Horse Publishing

To order additional copies contact:
Dollmasters, PO Box 2319, Annapolis, MD 21404
Tel. 800-966-3655 Fax 410-571-9605
www.dollmasters.com

Special tributes are extended to Kirsten Stadelhofer, long-time curator of the Legoland Museum of Antique Dolls, Dollhouses, and Toys and to Marianne & Jurgen Cieslik who first told us about this exceptional museum many years ago, and who have featured the dolls and toys in many articles in Cieslik's Puppenmagazin, German Doll Encyclopedia, and Lehmann Toys.

To George who has always understood 'play well.'

This book is based upon an antique doll collection auctioned by Theriault's of Annapolis, Maryland.

Art Direction & Design: Travis Hammond
Photography: Gerald Nelson
Production Design: Tucker Jones

$129
ISBN: 1-931503-38-9
Printed in Hong Kong

Table of Contents

VOLUME ONE

VOLUME TWO

Introduction

It was 1932 in the then-remote little village of Billund in Denmark, a several-hour train ride from Copenhagen. A young man, Ole' Kirk Christiansen, was starting up a small company to make wooden toys, ironing boards and stepladders. A few years later his son, Godfredt, then 12 years old, joined him. They named their company, LEGO, a simple Danish word that translates into English as "play well".

Play well and work hard they did. Much changed, of course. Ironing boards and stepladders went by the wayside. Wood became plastic. The interlocking bricks trademarked LEGO were born. By the 1960's Ole' Kirk and Godfredt's small-town company had grown into one of the greatest international toy firms.

To show appreciation to the worldwide public that had embraced their toy, the Christiansen family determined to open a public park whose purpose would be to celebrate the joy of play. There would be beautiful walkways, picnic areas, and amusement rides. And, in an extraordinary gesture honoring playthings of the past, there would be the Legoland Museum of Antique Dolls, Toys, and

Dollhouses. The acquisition of two fine private collections, the antique doll and dollhouse collection of Estrid Faurholt, and the antique toy collection of Helge Hess, the Danish artist, formed the nucleus of that Museum.

There weren't too many doll or dollhouse collectors in Copenhagen in the 1950's. That is, according to one woman who was. That was Estrid Faurholt, an intrepid collector and methodical researcher, who wrote in her *Book of Dolls and Dollhouses* in 1967 that she knew of only one other doll collector in Denmark, and that was both a blessing, because the lack of competition made many wonderful dolls available to her, and a lonely curse.

Certainly what we know about dolls and dollhouses has evolved since Estrid Faurholt wrote about her collection, but that she showed a remarkable prescience for rarities and special treasures, and that she respected each dollhouse and doll's history remains a constant truth.

That reverence was made clear in a story she related many years later to Kirsten Stadelhofer, curator of the Legoland Museum:

> *"I have collected dolls since I was five years old. It all started one Christmas when I came into the kitchen where my mother was baking and she said, 'Oh, little Estrid, go into the bathroom a minute and fetch me a towel.' The bathroom was, at that time, a place that was only heated up once a week, when the family would bathe. But anyway, I had to go in there now and what do you think I saw at once when I went in? A most beautiful doll house. I ran out to the kitchen and shouted that I knew what I was to have as a Christmas gift. 'No, no', said mother. 'That's for little Ellen that lives upstairs. She must not see it before Christmas. Therefore her parents have hidden it down here.' Oh, how I cried and cried every night under my blankets when no one could see me. Then, came Christmas Day. Everyone received Christmas gifts, except me. As soon as I had informed mother of that horrific situation, she opened the big double doors of our parlor, with a strange gleam in her eye. There stood the dollhouse that had been my grandmothers when she was a child. The delightful*

light-blue kitchen still smelled of fresh paint. The little furniture and dolls were set very primly in their place. Everything was just so wonderful and delightful! I honestly believe that the shock I first had that day has followed after me all of my life." (Grandmother's Dollhouse appears as #102 on page 46-47 of this book).

The core collection of the wonderful antique toys of Legoland Museum was also that of a private Danish collector, Helge Hess. He had scoured Europe in the post-war years and beyond for toy treasures from the golden age of Europe's toymaking industry. His collection was of a broad scope ranging from optical and steam toys, from delightful little tin penny toys to early carved bone and paper mache balance and tumbling toys. The mechanical tin toys of Germany and France were a special pleasure, and in viewing his remarkable collection of early works by Ernst Paul Lehmann it is possible to enter the mind of the toy creator, as well as the mind of the collector who gathered them together. There is The Performing Sea Lion that Lehmann watched, as he sat on the porch of the Cliff House in San Franciso overlooking the Pacific Coast rocky shore. Fascinated by the performance, Lehmann later transformed it into a simple, but not-so-simple toy. There is Tut-Tut, the officious irritating driver that still exists today, and there is the Naughty Boy, who grabs the steering wheel of his Papa's car as they ride along. Each of these presents a vignette that is as realistic as it is humorous, as does The Anxious Bride and the more than 35 other Lehmann toys that are in the collection.

And, too, today's collectors cannot help but wonder at individual craftsman that created a simple folk art doll or toy, perhaps a hand-drawn painting for a dollhouse or a horse and cart, sturdy, heavy, workmanlike. For whose child? What is its history? Estrid Faurholt wondered at the painted red spots hidden beneath the costume on the simple cloth body of the hand-carved wooden doll (#794, page 267, this book), conjecturing that the original child owner may have had measles, and in an empathetic gesture, the doll's body was dabbed with spots to match. Serious scholars may scoff at these musings, but true collectors understand, grasping to capture the true sense of each object they own.

It is nearly 40 years ago that the Museum opened. It has been a must-go, must-see destination for doll, dollhouse and toy collectors worldwide since that time. Its imaginative exhibitions as well as its rarities have inspired collectors worldwide. Dollhouses kept intact as though real people had walked out of their doors 100 years ago, and nothing had changed since. Toys creatively displayed in clear bubbles suspended from the rafters so viewers could see from all sides, even the mechanical works at the bottom. And dolls standing serenely watchful or posed in play, as though 200-year-old sisters stood guard on the 100-year-old "youngsters". To this haven of quietude, worldwide visitors had continued to flock each year.

Last year the beloved Legoland Museum closed its doors forever (with the single exception of the dollhouse Titania's Palace that will remain at the Legoland Park in Billund). The Lego Foundation, ever mindful of the Museum origins, determined that its treasures would best be cared for by the worldwide collectors who had yearned over them over four decades. Perhaps Estrid Faurholt had said it best, some 50 years ago when describing her dollhouse collection. "My collection...consists of nine Danish, eight English, three German and one American house, and of two German, one Dutch, one French, and the rest Danish rooms. So you see it is rather universal." (Jacobs, *A History of Doll Houses*, 1953).

In determining to return the Legoland Museum of Antique Dolls, Dollhouses and Toys to the hands of private collectors, the Legoland Foundation is truly fulfilling its role as keeper of the past. Older than us, the objects have their own lives. That we respect and care for them while they are in our care, ensuring that they will carry their message to the next generation, is all that is ultimately asked of any collector.

Yet, finally, in homage to the remarkable Legoland Museum, to remember its parts and to relish the extraordinary sum of its parts, this two-volume book is created. Enjoy the voyage, play well.

1. *A Pristine German Bisque Doll with Danish Sailor Costume*

13" (33 cm.) Bisque socket head, brown glass sleep eyes, open mouth, four porcelain teeth, blonde mohair wig, composition ball-jointed body. Condition: generally excellent, original wig, body and body finish in near pristine condition. Marks: Germany HH S&H 2/0. Comments: Heinrich Handwerck, circa 1912. The doll, with beautiful dewy patina of bisque, in appealing cabinet size, wears her original red and blue flannel sailor costume with sailor cap bearing the name "Maagen" in gilt letters. "Maagen" featured prominently in the sea history of Denmark, its most romantic appearance as the name of the 18th century Danish Royal Yacht. $500/800

2. *Pair of German Bisque Miniature Dolls in Original Costumes*

5" (13 cm.) Each has bisque socket head with painted facial features, blue eyes, closed mouth, mohair wig, five piece paper mache body, painted shoes and stockings. Marks: 13a. Comments: Germany, circa 1910. The dolls each wear an original tan and brown felt uniform with braid trim, matching caps with passamenterie, and carry little soft-metal silver swords. $500/700

3. *German Lithographed-over-Wood Elevator Doll House by Gottschalk*

18" (46 cm.) 18" x 10" x 8". The wooden two story house with painted blue roof features gilded pressed cardboard porch railings on each balconied floor, wooden porch railings, faux marble base, two hinged doors with classic Gottschalk door knockers, glass windows on front and sides, well detailed lithographed architectural features including attic window. The front hinges open to reveal two rooms and two foyer rooms with an elevator at the back that operates from a turning lever at the house exterior. The house has all original interior wall and floor papers, and lace curtains. The elevator functions. Germany, Gottschalk, circa 1900. $900/1300

3 detail.

3, 5.

4. Miniature Tin Lithographed Coffee Grinder

2" (5 cm.) Tin toy coffee grinder with faux-mahogany finish has a copper bowl top, wooden tipped tin handle, and pull-out drawer. Excellent condition. Circa 1900. $200/300

5. German Bisque Child by Kammer and Reinhardt in Original Sailor Costume

23" (58 cm.) Bisque socket head, blue glass sleep eyes, open mouth, four porcelain teeth, brunette mohair wig, composition ball-jointed body. Marks: Simon & Halbig K*R 62. Condition: generally excellent, original body finish except hands retouched. Comments: Kammer and Reinhardt, circa 1910. The doll wears her original red and blue serge sailor costume, brown leather boots. $600/900

6. *German Bisque Pouty Character By Gebruder Heubach with Store Label*

14" (36 cm.) Solid domed bisque socket head with painted and sculpted short brown boyish hair, intaglio small blue eyes, well-defined sculpting of pouty features, closed mouth with downcast lips, full cheeks, composition ball-jointed toddler body with side-hip jointing. Condition: generally excellent, some body retouch. Marks: 7759 Heubach (square mark) Germany 5. Comments: Gebruder Heubach, circa 1912, the toddler pouty wears antique linen smock with embrodiery, red woolen cap and stockings, black leather shoes stamped "Legetojs-Huset Theodor Thorngreen 46, Vimmelskaffet, 46." $600/900

7. *German Tin Lithographed Garden Room with Bisque Dolls*

10" (25 cm.) 10" x 10" x 8". Dolls 3 1/2" . A white-painted tin frame roof and trellis is attached to a lithographed tin base painted to resemble a grassy ground. The trellis and roof are decorated with faux-flowers and leaves, and arranged within the setting are original green tin chairs, long bench, green table and flower pot. Seated on the chairs as though enjoying nature are three all-bisque dolls, one with glass eyes, with mohair wigs, jointed limbs, antique costumes. Condition: generally excellent. Comments: Germany, circa 1910, a rare and wonderfully preserved doll house garden accessory or showcase for miniature dolls. $700/1000

8. *German All-Bisque Doll with Cobalt Blue Eyes and Swivel Head*

5" (13 cm.) Bisque swivel head on bisque torso, cobalt blue glass inset eyes, slightly parted lips, porcelain teeth, mohair wig, peg-jointed bisque arms and legs, painted shoes and stockings. Condition: generally excellent, flake on underside of right middle finger. Marks: 12 31. Comments: Germany, circa 1900, the swivel head boy wears factory original blue and red knit costume and cap. $300/400

8.

9. *German Bisque Pouty Child by Kling*

15" (38 cm.) Solid domed bisque shoulder head turned to the right, brown glass inset eyes, closed mouth with pouty downcast lips, blonde mohair wig, commercial muslin stitch-jointed body with bisque lower arms and legs, antique costume. Condition: generally excellent, right thumb broken. Marks: 166 4. Comments: C.F. Kling & Co., circa 1895, a beguiling expression with lovely bisque, rare body style with bisque feet. $600/900

8.

9.

10.

10. *German Bisque Dollhouse Man with Wooden Horse*

5" (13 cm.) Bisque shoulder head portraying adult man with black painted hair and facial features, sculpted brown moustache, muslin body, bisque lower limbs, along with carved wooden glass-eyed horse with finely executed brown horsehair finish and decorative leather and silver saddle and harness. Condition: generally excellent. Comments: Germany, circa 1900, the man wears his factory original blue woolen greatcoat and trousers. $500/800

11. *German Blue and White Porcelain Kitchenware*

4" (10 cm.) Of white porcelain with cobalt blue decorations, including porcelain hanging rack with wooden handled utensils comprising two spoons, two sieved spoons, mallet, and a silver-tipped candle snuffer. Also included is a double-handled sieved bowl and floral-decorated cutting board with hanging hole. One spoon has tiny chip. Germany, circa 1890. $500/700

12. *German Bisque Boy by Kling with Brown Glass Eyes*

13" (33 cm.) Bisque shoulderhead turned to the right, deeply sculpted blonde hair with tousled curls, brown glass inset eyes, closed mouth with painted downcast lips, kid gusset-jointed body with bisque lower arms, wearing an antique blue woolen sailor suit, leather shoes with silver buckles. Marks: 190 K (in bell symbol). Condition: generally excellent, left thumb chipped. Comments: C.F. Kling & Co., circa 1885, an especially appealing facial expression enhanced by fine bisque and rich enhancing glaze on sculpted hair. $400/500

11.

12.

13. *Fine Large German Kitchen with Original Wooden Furnishings*

34"w. x15"h. x17"d. The wooden framed kitchen has a painted floor and walls to simulate a fancy designed tile, 4 paned windows at the sides, and 5 blue and cream wooden hanging shelves of various dimensions, two with notched plate holders. The furnishings include a cast iron stove with copper towel bar and silvered decorations, and an ensemble of blue and cream wooden furniture, viz. table and 2 stools, 2 counters, work table with shelf and one chair. Kitchenware and equipment includes a tin stenciled hanging cabinet, wooden slaw board, blue wooden broom, brushes, whisk, 2 pewter candlesticks, lidded tureen, 11 pewter plates and bowls, pewter-edged glass bowl with pressed designs, 3 white porcelain canisters, cutlery, 4 napkins and rings, brass coffee mill and tea kettle, 4 tin lidded pots, 11 copper pots, pans and kettles, 3 copper molds, tin coal scuttle with wooden handles, 5 white porcelain platters, 2 blue enamelware pans and a tin wall telephone. Germany, early 20th century. $3000/4000

14. *German Bisque Doll in Diminutive Size*

9" (23 cm.) Bisque shoulder head of plump-faced child with very pale complexion, blonde sculpted hair waved away from face into short pageboy curls, exposed ears, painted blue eyes, closed mouth, muslin stitch-jointed body, bisque lower limbs, wearing lovely blue muslin printed gown and hand-stitched undergarments. Condition: generally excellent. Comments: Germany, circa 1875, a rare variation of the model known as Alice in Wonderland has unpainted hair ribbon. $300/500

13 details.

15. *Fine Early Wooden Hand-Painted Scandanavian Chest*

5" (13 cm.) Pinewood four-drawer chest of unusual construction with protruding drawer ends and simple silver ring pulls, has a fine original painted finish of blue/grey background with gold edging and fancifully painted flowers and leaves in variegated colors. The design is on the drawer fronts, top, and both sides. Excellent condition. Mid-19th century. $300/500

16. *Five Early Miniature Irons*

4.5" (11 cm.) Of heavy cast brass or iron, in various sizes (largest 4.5"), the group includes three flat irons (two with cast iron fancy handles), and two irons with hinged door at the back for insertion of coals to keep the irons warm. Also included are two cast iron trivets. Excellent condition. Mid-19th century. $400/700

17. *German Porcelain Doll House Lady with Table and Glassware*

6" (15 cm.) Thick paste porcelain shoulder head lady with slightly tinted complexion has brown painted hair drawn in wide loops below her ears into a chignon bun at back of head, painted facial features, elongated throat, sloping shoulders, muslin stitch-jointed body, porcelain limbs, antique costume. Included is a Biedermeier pedestal table with white blown glass tableware. Excellent condition. Germany, circa 1870. $400/700

14, 15.

16.

17.

18 details.

18. English Wooden Dollhouse Known as "The Sparrowe's House of Ipswich"

24"h (including chimney) x 27"w x 12"d. The long rectangular wooden two story house rests upon a wooden platform, and features a second floor that crops out over the first floor, steeped roof with painted shingle effect, four dormer windows at the front, and three dormer windows at the back, along with two 6-stack chimneys. There is a painted brick design around the base of the house, and thick-painted pargeting overall with ornamental scenes and figures. The house front features 4 rounded bay windows on the second floor with tiny painted panes and 7 smaller windows on the lst floor. At the back are 6 large windows with faux-leaded panes. The left side is fairly plain with 5 windows of various sizes and shapes, while the right side is richly decorated and features a curved bay window on the second floor. Innumerable rich sculpted designs decorate the front and right side of the house, including scenes of villagers, boaters, children, men on horseback, various mythological figures, Cupid at play and abundant garlands and columns. There is a painted coat of arms on the front center of the house. The center hinges open (separately for each floor) for interior access to four large rooms and two center foyers with central staircase. The rooms are richly paneled, with four fireplaces, faux-brick flooring and half-timbered ceilings. The house is a miniature of the actual Sparrowe's House of Ipswich, England built in 1567 (and still standing) and was one of about 20 Sparrowe's dollhouses created by F. Tibbenham, Ltd about 1930. Tibbenham, an early 20th century Ipswich craftsman who specialized in reproductions of 16th century furniture, may have made the houses as a presentation of his quality of work. One existing example is at the Sparrowe's House Museum, another is at the Strong Museum in Rochester, and this example is known to have come from the Estrid Faurholt Collection of Copenhagen that was acquired by the Legoland Museum. A rare and superbly executed piece in fine condition. England, circa 1930. $8000/12,000

18 detail.

19. *Important Carved Walnut Doll House Furnishings in the Tudor Style*

6" (15 cm.) Sixteen pieces of dark walnut furniture each is richly embellished with carvings or panels. Included is a 6"h. canopy bed with silver covered and embroidered pillow, large four door cupboard, hooded cradle, blanket chest, long tavern table and bench, four side chairs, child's chair, two arm chairs, high chair, two small side tables, open-top cupboard, side-angle bench and paneled two door kitchen cupboard. Also included is a 5" German porcelain doll house lady with fancy coiffure and original silk costume. Excellent condition. Probably early 20th century. $600/900

20. *Two Rare German Wooden-Bodied Porcelain Dolls*

6" (15 cm.) Each has thick paste pressed porcelain shoulder head with black sculpted hair deeply looped around the face and softly pulled into chignon at back of head (one with exposed ears), painted facial features, wooden body with shapely waist, dowel-jointing at shoulders, elbows, hips, and knees, porcelain lower limbs, painted flat orange shoes, each with original antique undergarments. Condition: one with hairline on shoulder plate, the other with reglue at right ankle. Comments: Germany, circa 1850, the rare pair includes one with extremely rare brown eyes. $800/1200

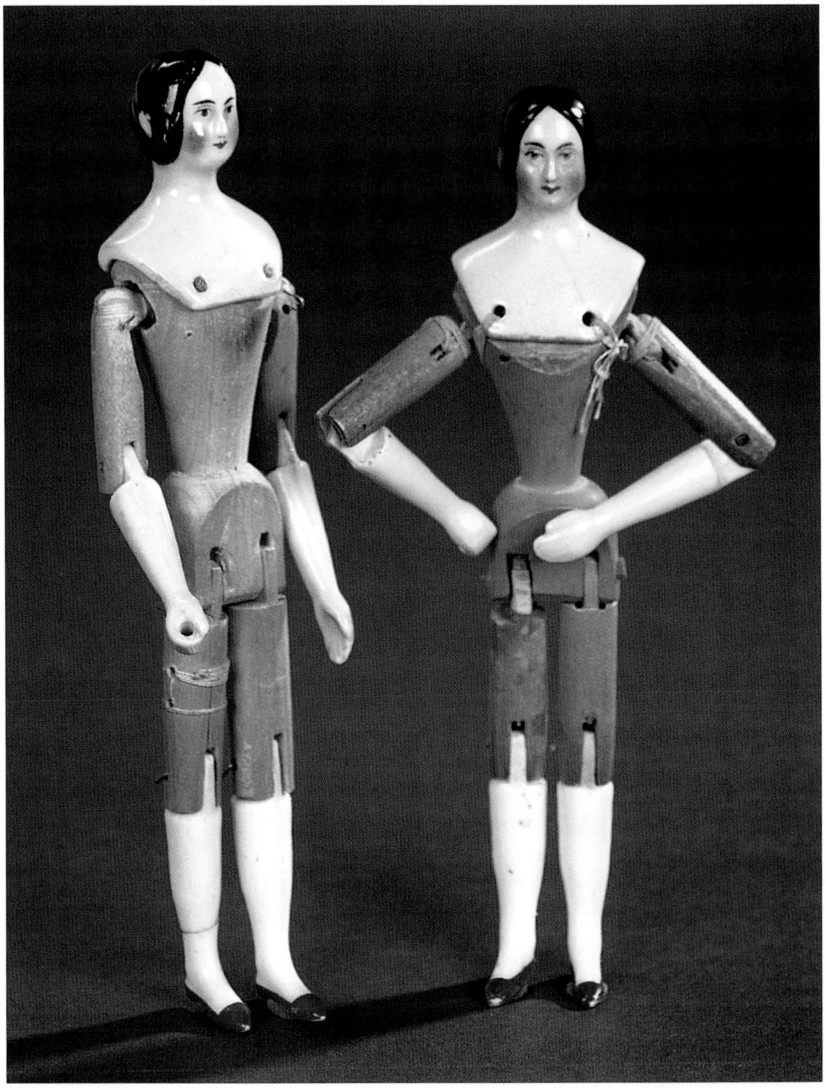

20.

21, 22.

21. *German Porcelain Doll with Pink Tinted Complexion*

15" (38 cm.) Thick paste hand-pressed porcelain with tinted complexion portrays a full-faced woman with strong throat, sculpted black hair in uniform finger curls, painted facial features, pale blue upper glancing eyes, early leather body, bisque lower arms. Condition: generally excellent, few paint rubs at back of hair, body of later era but appropriately sized. Comments: Germany, circa 1860, the doll wears a fine early sheer muslin rose gown, undergarments, leather boots. $500/800

24.

22. *Petite German Porcelain Lady with Original Costume*

12" (30 cm.) Pink-tinted porcelain shoulder head with rounded facial modeling, short sculpted black hair in uniform finger curls, painted blue eyes, blushed cheeks, pink-kid body with shapely form. Condition: generally excellent. Comments: Germany, circa 1865, very beautiful complexion and unusual detail of facial painting, the doll wears antique costume, apron, undergarments, slippers. $400/500

23.

23. *German Porcelain Doll House Doll with Wooden Dowel-Jointed Body*

5.5" (14 cm.) Thick paste porcelain shoulder head with pink tinted complexion, black hair sculpted into long finger curls, painted facial features, shapely wooden torso and upper limbs, porcelain lower limbs with painted flat orange shoes, dowel-jointing at shoulders, elbows, hips and knees. Condition: generally excellent. Comments: Germany, circa 1860, the doll wears her original muslin print dress and undergarments. $600/900

24. *German Porcelain Doll House Doll and Decorated Tin Rocking Chair*

6" (15 cm.) Porcelain shoulder head doll with short curly hair, painted features, muslin body and porcelain limbs is wearing her original costume and undergarments. Included is a rare tin rocking chair in the so-called Boston Rocker style with stenciled and floral painted decorations. Circa 1890. $300/500

25.

25 detail.

26.

25. *English Wooden Miniature "The James Legg Pastry Shop"*

12" (30 cm.) 12" x 14" x 8". The single-room wooden framed shop has an elaborately constructed store front with large built-out four-paned window to be used for display, a paneled front door with four glass windows that hinges open inward, columnar sides and original green paint with white lettering "92 James Legg 92". Inside are built in display shelves against the back wall, a long store counter, and a small bench. There is a paper roll, scale, plates of pastries, tin lithographed biscuit tins, and a German bisque doll house Baker in his factory original costume. Excellent condition. English, circa 1900. $1200/1800

26. *Miniature Grodnertal Wooden Doll in Early Sedan Chair*

5" (13 cm.) The all-wooden doll has painted-over-gesso complexion, facial features and hair, elongated throat, dowel-jointing at shoulders, elbows, hips and knees, painted white stockings and orange flat shoes, and is wearing a (frail) early muslin dress and matching cap. The doll is preserved inside her tapestry covered wooden sedan chair with glass windows and original carrying sticks. Condition: original finish with some wear on face. Comments: circa 1840, a captivating and rare small size of both doll and her carriage. $400/500

27 detail.

27. *Early Grodnertal Wooden Doll as Doll and Notions Peddler Lady*

7" (18 cm.) An all-wooden doll with painted black hair highlighted by spit curls onto forehead and yellow tuck comb has painted complexion and facial features, all-wooden body with dowel-jointing at shoulders, elbows, hips and knees, and wearing early brown cotton print gown. Condition: generally excellent, original finish perfectly preserved. Comments: Gordnertal doll, circa 1850, presented for the English market as a peddler lady offering sewing notions and dolls. On her table are arranged a myriad of tiny laces, ribbons and buttons, sewing tools such as tiny scissors, various papers with lettered names "Robert", "Margaret" and "John", several tiny doll costumes, and five tiny dolls including two mini Grodnertal woodens. $900/1300

27.

28.

28. *Miniature Grodnertal Wooden Doll with Early Cradle*

4" (10 cm.) An all-wooden doll with black painted hair having curl above each ear, paint-over-gesso complexion with painted facial features, blushed cheeks, dowel-jointed wooden arms and legs, painted flat shoes, antique muslin shirt. Condition: generally excellent, some minor craquelure on forehead. Comments; Grodnertal, circa 1850, the well-preserved little doll is resting in an early hooded walnut cradle. $400/500

29. *German Bisque Dollhouse Gentleman with Modeled Top Hat*

6.5" (17 cm.) Bisque shoulderhead of adult man with blond painted hair beneath a tall grey top hat with feather trim and yellow band and brim, painted facial features, muslin body, bisque lower limbs. Condition: generally excellent, tiny flakes on feather side and boot tip. Comments: Germany, circa 1880, an early model with rare model of hat, wearing factory original caped greatcoat and trousers. $300/400

30. *19th Century Wooden Horse and Carriage in Appealing Size*

11" (28 cm.) A hide-covered wooden horse with glass eyes and elaborate leather harness is pulling a maple wood carriage with metal spoked wheels, silver banding and original carpet and seat cushion. Condition: generally excellent. Comments: circa 1875, an unusually diminutive size in well preserved condition. $400/500

31. *German Porcelain Doll in Original Folklore Costume and Coiffe of Amager, Denmark*

14" (36 cm.) Porcelain shoulder head with short black painted curly hair in boyish fashion, exposed ears, painted facial features with slightly smiling expression, muslin stitch-jointed body, leather arms. Condition: generally excellent. Comments: Germany, circa 1865, the doll is wearing its original folklore costume of Amager which includes undergarments including woolen petticoats, silk embroidered padded blouse, white handmade apron, silk ribbon streamers, and an elaborate coiffe. $700/1000

32. *German Porcelain Doll in Folklore Costume of Amager, Denmark*

13" (33 cm.) Porcelain shoulder head with short black painted hair in boyish fashion, stippled curls around the forehead, painted facial features, closed mouth, muslin body, porcelain lower arms and legs with painted flat black shoes. Condition: generally excellent. Comments: Germany, circa 1865, the doll is wearing its original elaborate folklore costume from the historic seaport island of Amager nearby Copenhagen comprising multi-layered undergarments, padded bodice under silk blouse with gilt braid and beads, hand-stitched apron, silk ribbon sash. $600/900

34.

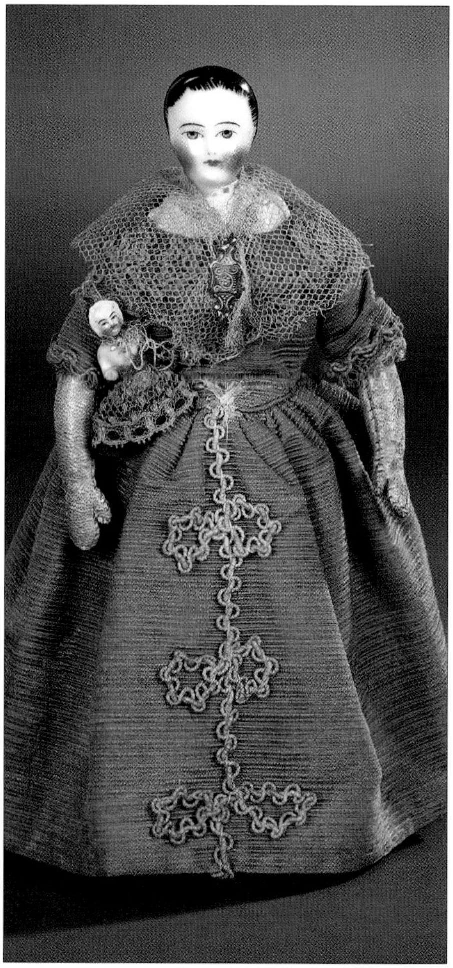

33.

33. *Petite Porcelain Doll in Original Costume for the French Market*

8" (20 cm.) Porcelain shoulder head with black painted short hair, stippled detail around the forehead, painted facial features with unusually large blue eyes, closed mouth, pink kid fashion style hand-stitched body with mitten hands. The doll wears her original patterned green gown with lace trim, ormolu brooch, undergarments, shoes, and carries a tiny bonnet doll (limbs broken). Condition: generally excellent. Comments: for the French market, circa 1860, the doll has fine original costume. $400/500

34 detail.

34. *Early Dollhouse Tin Kitchen with Built-In Oven*

13" (33 cm.) 13"h x 22"w x 12"s. A heavy tin metal kitchen has embossed designs on green/ brown painted walls, embossed tile-patterned floor, and blue exterior walls. Built on the side corner of the kitchen is a large stone-painted oven with open hearth, closed oven door, stove top, and warming shelf. There is a large plate shelf and hanging rack at the back, and three hanging racks that are permanently attached to the walls, as is the wide counter at the back wall. The kitchen contains a wooden table and chair, butcher three-legged block, china head doll, and a vast assortment of kitchenware in earthenware, pewter, copper and tin. Germany, circa 1865. $2000/3000

35. *A Late 19th Century Cabinet Doll House with Provenance Known as "The Koppel House"*

49"h. x 25"w. x 14"d. A simple pinewood cabinet with glass-front double front doors has 6 rooms on 4 floors; the two bottom floors have glass windows at the sides and painted windows at the upper floors. The lower floor is the kitchen with typically larger scale contents including a metal stove with brass oven doors, brass towel bar and a kettle, 2 pots and a boiler, 2 wooden work tables, hanging wooden shelf and plate rack, hanging utensil rack, 2 tin scalloped edge shelves and 2 matching corner shelves, and equipment comprising wooden plates, tray, cutting tray, bucket, salt, 2 tin sieves, iron wood, porcelain rolling pin and a copper mold. On other floors are 2 bedrooms, a large salon, dining room and breakfast room, each with old paper and curtains, electrified with 2 chandeliers. The furnishings include: 13 pieces Biedermeier case goods such as baby bed, marble top buffet with ivory columns, corner étagère, 2 pianos and a game table; 8 piece Biedermeier seated pieces; very fine early walnut dining pedestal table with 5 chairs and settee; early wooden Gothic style bedroom suite with canopy bed, corner cupboard, blanket chest, and deacon's bench. Accessories include an unusual tin fire screen, shaving mirror, miniature art glass vase, brass wine cupboard and hanging vitrine, magazine

35 details.

rack, brass bird cage, fancy silvered compote, brass and copper parlor stove, and clocks. There are four dollhouse dolls. In the living room there is a miniature newspaper "Die Gartenlaube" in which is inscribed a birthday greeting from Aunt Henriette Ree to Doritha Koppel on her 4th birthday in 1878. According to Museum records, the house was later acquired by a family Nielsen, probably from the Danish island Langeland, who later emigrated to America. In the mid-20th century Estrid Faurholt acquired the house, and later it passed to the Lego Foundation Museum along with the entire Faurholt Collection. Circa 1880. $7500/12,500

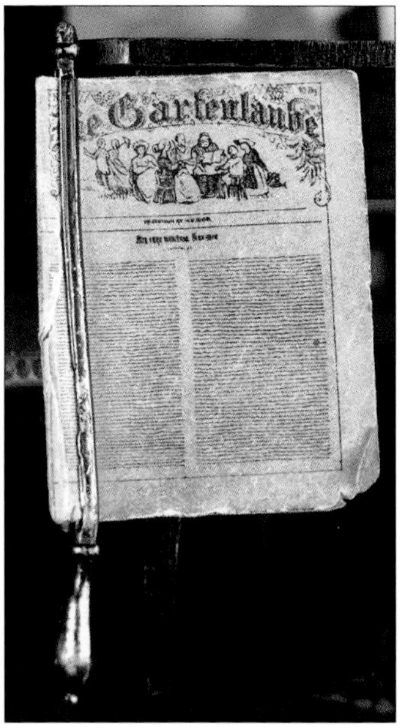

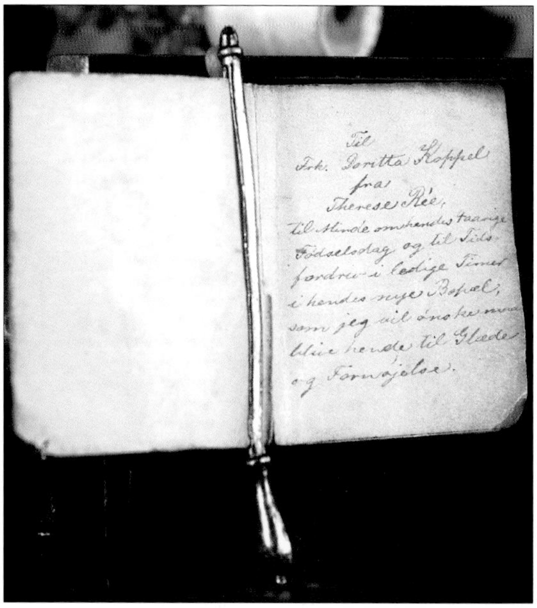

35 details.

36.

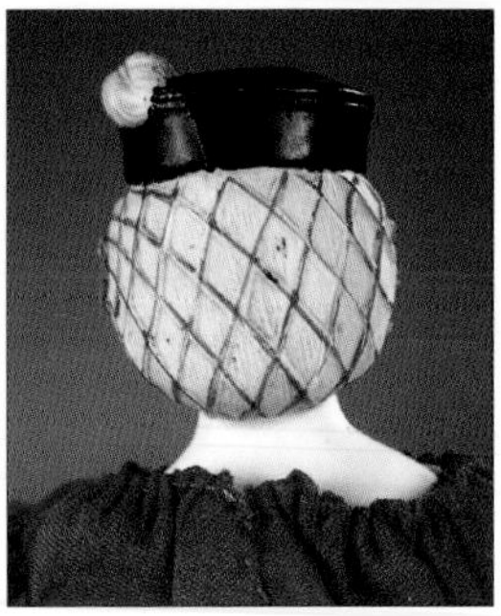

36 detail.

36. *Petite German Bisque Lady with Fancy Hat and Snood*

10" (25 cm.) Pale bisque shoulder head with blonde sculpted hair captured under a magenta painted snood with decorative blue bows at the side, and topped with a black toque hat decorated with a mauve/white large sculpted plume, painted facial features, leather body, wearing antique gown and undergarments. Condition: generally excellent. Comments: Germany, circa 1870, exceptionally rare model with exquisite detail of painting of expressive facial features, fancy bonnet and snood. $800/1100

37. *Miniature German Bisque Dollhouse Lady with Fancy Snood*

7" (18 cm.) Bisque shoulder head with slender facial modeling and elongated throat, blonde sculpted hair drawn away from face and captured under a painted blue snood with mauve and white lustre tassels and feathers, painted facial features, muslin body, bisque limbs, antique costume comprising hand-stitched gown and undergarments appear to be original. Condition: generally excellent. Comments: Germany, circa 1870, the rare model has exquisitely executed painting and modeling, very expressive features. $500/800

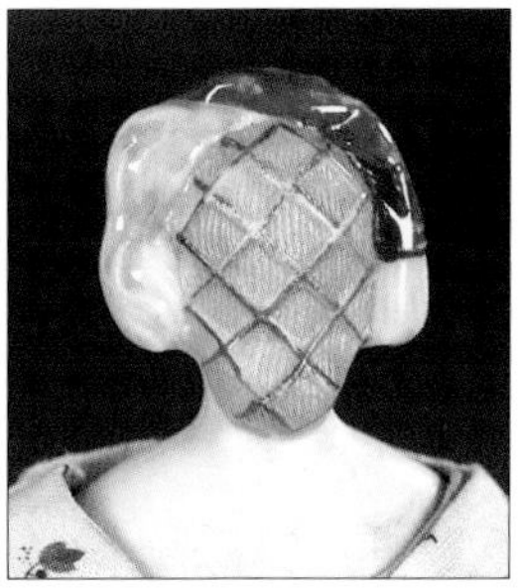

37 detail.

37.

38.

39.

40.

38. *19th Century Bone Miniature Dollhouse Accessories*

2" (5 cm.) The miniature accessories, made of carved bone or ivory, comprise a game table with tri-leg pedestal having chess pieces on table surface, pair of candlesticks, and fancy birdcage with perch, carrying handle and hinged door opening to the tiny bird. Excellent condition, the chess table underside is reinforced with plaster. Circa 1875. $400/600

39. *Miniature Biedermeier Upright Piano as Music Box*

5" (13 cm.) Wooden upright piano with opening keyboard cover is decorated in the Renaissance Revival style with cutwork at the front for good musical sound. The manivelle style music box, when wound by the porcelain knob handle at the back, creates a lovely sound with a good quality music box. Excellent condition, original finish well preserved and music functions well. Circa 1880, a rare form of music box as dollhouse furnishing. $500/700

40 detail.

40. *Fine Early Furnished Dollhouse Room with Stenciled Cabinet*

13" (33 cm.) A thick wooden box-shaped room has a slanted ceiling with glass top and two back wall windows to allow natural light, hinged double doors that appear as curtained windows when closed, and form a larger wing when opened. The exterior of the room is paint-grained and stencil-outlined to appear as an exotic wood, and there is a fancy scrolled decoration at the crest. The interior has original painting with trompe l'oeil wainscot, blue painted walls, and fancily painted floor to simulate a tapestry carpet. The house is furnished with a lovely Biedermeier davenport slant front desk, small table with drop leaf sides, three Biedermeier chairs, settee and a corner etagere. Decorations include an ormolu birdcage with bird, ormolu wall sconces, tin pedestal table, hanging clock, and pictures. There are three dollhouse dolls including early bisque doll with brown sculpted hair and original costume. Circa 1860, a rare style of miniature room with original finish well preserved. $1500/2000

41.

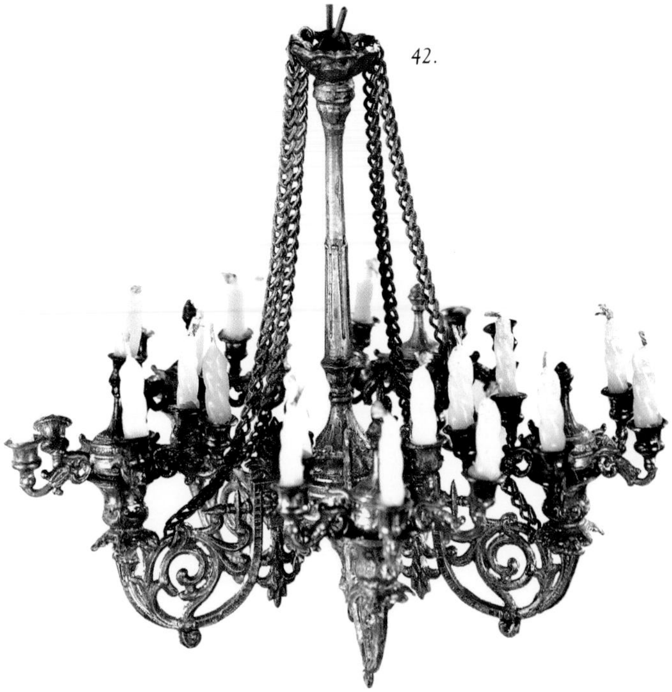

42.

43.

41. *Early Crystal and Brass Hanging Chandelier*

8" (20 cm.) An exceptional hanging chandelier suitable for use in larger dollhouse or in room setting with fashion dolls, has graduated size prismatic crystal beads arranged in cascading rows from a darkened brass frame and centered by a large crystal prism at the bottom center. Excellent condition. Circa 1900. $400/500

42. *Elaborate Miniature Five Arm Hanging Chandelier with Removable Candelabra*

5" (13 cm.) A gilded soft metal hanging chandelier has five arms each on elaborately scrolled frames that are attached to a center rod and decorated with looping chains. Each arm has its own miniature five-arm candelabra with elaborate designs to match the center piece, and two of these are removable for use as the centerpiece candelabra on a mantel or table. Excellent condition, some paint wear to gilding. Circa 1890. $300/400

43. *Hanging Chandelier with Cut Glass Globe*

9" (23 cm.) 13"l. overall. 4" globe. Designed to suspend from the ceiling on brass chain links, the half-egg shaped glass globe has an embossed brass edging and is decorated with a cut glass sunburst design enhanced with gold paint. Excellent condition, slight wear to gold paint. Circa 1900. $300/400

44. *Three Early Miniature Albums*

2" (5 cm.) Comprising two photograph albums with ormolu fretwork covers that hinge open to reveal contents of fancy matte pages inset with sepia toned miniature photographs of old master paintings; along with a journal or autograph book with unusual embossed leather cover having a scene of family life in an old European kitchen of mid-19th century, with attached miniature pencil. Excellent condition. Late 19th century. $400/600

45. *Superb Large Ormolu Birdcage with Feeders and Birdbath*

3" (8 cm.) A large birdcage of gilt ormolu metal has very fancy spindles in a sunray fashion, two revolving bird-feeders at the outside, and a metal birdbath inside upon whose rim is perched an exotic bird. The cage is unusual both for its size and for its design and added accessory pieces. Circa 1890. $400/600

44.

46. Carved Bone Dressing Table with Accessories

4.5" (11 cm.) A fine carved bone or ivory dressing table has an attached mirror with carved brackets and beaded edging, fretwork drawers that actually open, very fancy carved legs, and three attached accessories on the table surface. Excellent condition. Circa 1885. $300/400

47. Miniature Ormolu Bird Cage and Table

5" (13 cm.) Resting upon a circular three-leg table with elaborately embossed designs around the apron and table top is a fancy ormolu bird cage with hanging loop, deeply embossed designs on its tray, and a large bird perched at the interior. Excellent condition. Circa 1890. $300/400

45.

48. Early German Porcelain Doll with Wooden Articulated Body

5" (13 cm.) Pink tinted hand-pressed porcelain shoulder head with long painted black hair looped behind the ears and cascading into long formed curls on the back, painted facial features, brown eyes, elongated throat, fully articulated wooden body with dowel jointing at shoulders, elbows, hips and knees, porcelain lower limbs, painted orange slippers, wearing an early green silk gown with lace trim, undergarments. Condition: generally excellent. Comments: Germany, circa 1855. $600/900

46.

49. *A Late 19th Century Furnished Doll House Known as "Vita's Eje"*

32"h (including steeple) 26"w x 13"l. A commercially-made wooden doll house with removable facade is finished on all four sides has lithographed paper simulating brown brick design and is very elaborately designed with 1st and 2nd floor porch and balcony on either side of the house, and an unusually angled tower at one corner with faux-stained glass windows surmounted by a steeple with widow's walk. The window frames and sills are carved wood, some with attached tin window boxes. There is carved gingerbread trim at the cornice. There is a miniature tin chocolate box serving as the porch mailbox and a Danish flag flying at the porch. The hinged angled attic roof is flat on top, with a dormer window having a tin railed balcony. There are 2 side porches, one on each floor, with arched windows and parquet porch floor. There are four windows at the rear, and a removable front. The interior comprises 4 large rooms and 2 attic rooms. The kitchen is located on the second floor with built-in shelves, a closet with door and a sink "pump" and is furnished with a maple table and a variety of kitchenware including seven greenware pieces. The first floor parlor and dining room are richly furnished, including a Maerklin heating stove, maple furniture, fancy upholstered parlor set, and each with a three arm

49 details.

chandelier and lace curtains. The bedroom has a 5-piece maple ensemble, chandelier and accessories. The house is well preserved, unrestored, with some lithographed paper wear and missing front door. Likely of German production, circa 1890, the house was owned by a Danish child as indicated by the name "Vita's Eje" hand-lettered over the front door and the Danish flag. The house was featured as one of the Faurholt "street of houses" in Jacobs' A *History of Doll Houses*, (1965, page 232). $4500/7500

49 details.

50, 51.

52, 53, 54.

50. *German Bisque Child by Kammer and Reinhardt*

21" (53 cm.) Bisque socket head, brown glass sleep eyes, open mouth, brunette mohair wig, composition ball-jointed body. Condition: generally excellent. Marks: K*R Simon & Halbig 53. Comments: Kammer and Reinhardt, circa 1910, the doll is wearing a lovely antique whitewear dress, bonnet, undergarments, shoes and stockings. $400/500

51. *German Bisque Character, 604, by Bahr and Proschild*

11" (28 cm.) Bisque socket head, brown glass sleep eyes, open mouth with beaded teeth, brunette mohair wig, composition baby body, lovely multi-layered antique baby costume of dotted Swiss. Condition: generally excellent. Marks: BP 604 2. Comments: Bahr and Proschild, circa 1910, included with the character-faced child is an early woven wicker park bench. $500/700

52. *Petite German Bisque Character "DIP" by Swaine and Co.*

8" (20 cm.) Bisque socket head, tiny blue glass sleep eyes, closed mouth with pouty expression, blonde mohair wig, composition baby body, wearing fine antique baby gown with undergarments, bonnet. Condition: generally excellent. Marks: DIP 2/0 Geschutz S&Co. German. Comments: Swaine and Co, circa 1915, an unusual petite size with original costume. $400/500

53. *German Bisque Character, 208, by Catterfelder Puppenfabrick*

12" (30 cm.) Bisque socket head, brown glass sleep eyes, open mouth, two teeth, brunette human hair, composition baby body, antique dotted Swiss baby costume. Condition: generally excellent. Marks: C.P. 208/30 Deponiert. Comments: Catterfelder Puppenfabrick, circa 1915, very expressive features with rich modeling. $400/500

54. *Woven Wicker Doll Carriage with Sunshade*

26" (66 cm.) 26"l. carriage of open-woven wicker wooden frame and muslin lining has iron undercarriage and spoken wheels, leather collapsible sunshade, wooden hand grip. Excellent condition, some paint wear to undercarriage. Circa 1900. $300/400

55. *German Bisque Doll with Blonde Hair and Blue Glass Eyes*

15" (38 cm.) Bisque shoulder head with sculpted short curly blonde hair, blue glass inset eyes, closed mouth with wistful expression, kid gusset-jointed body, bisque lower arms. Condition: generally excellent, small eye rim flake at right eyelid, one finger chipped. Comments: attributed to Kling, circa 1885, the doll is wearing a beautiful antique dress, undergarments, matching bonnet. $300/500

56. *German Bisque Child, 131, by Kling with Brown Glass Eyes*

18" (46 cm.) Bisque shoulder head with short blonde sculpted hair having deeply sculpted bangs, large brown glass eyes, closed mouth, modeled ears, kid pin-jointed body, composition lower legs, bisque lower arms. Condition: generally excellent, three fingers chipped.

Marks: 131 K (in bell) 5. Comments: Kling, circa 1890, the large brown eyes enhance her beautiful expression, wearing antique dress and undergarments, shoes, stockings. $400/500

57. *German All-Bisque Miniature Doll with Pouty Expression*

5.5" (14 cm.) Solid domed bisque swivel head, cobalt blue glass inset eyes, closed mouth with wistful expression, blonde mohair wig, peg-jointed limbs, painted white stockings and black one-strap shoes, antique costume. Condition: generally excellent. Marks: 2. Comments: Germany, circa 1890. $400/500

58. *German All-Bisque Doll with Swivel Head and Original Costume*

5" (13 cm.) Solid domed bisque swivel head, brown glass inset eyes, closed mouth, blonde mohair wig, peg-jointed bisque arms and legs, painted white stockings and black one-strap shoes. Condition: generally excellent. Marks: 31-32 12. Comments: Gebruder Kuhnlenz, circa 1895, the swivel head doll is in all original unplayed with condition with beautifully preserved wig and costume. $600/900

55, 56.

59. *German All-Bisque Miniature by Kestner*

6" (15 cm.) One piece bisque head and torso, painted facial features, closed mouth, blonde mohair wig, peg-jointed bisque arms and legs, painted stockings and brown two-strap shoes with black rosettes, wearing antique knit dress, cotton undergarments. Condition: generally excellent. Marks: 130 5 3/4 (head) 5 3/4 (limbs). Comments: Kestner, circa 1910. $300/400

57.

58.

59.

60.

62 detail.

60. *Grodnertal Peddler Lady with Basket of Notions*

11" (28 cm.) All-wooden doll with painted black hair with shaded curls around the face, paint over gesso complexion and facial features, dowel-jointing at shoulders, elbows, hips and knees. The doll is wearing her original homespun and woolen costume with flannel bonnet, undergarments, and is carrying a woven basket upon which are arranged a myriad of tiny sewing notions and related goods such as tiny toys. The doll and basket are posed upon a wooden base. Condition: generally excellent, tip of tuck comb broken off. Comments: Grodnertal, circa 1850, the doll was created for the English market. $1100/1700

61.

61. *Tiny German Bisque Dollhouse Doll in Amager Folklore Costume*

4" (10 cm.) Bisque shoulder head with brown sculpted hair arranged in deep curls with painted black ribbon at crest, painted facial features, muslin body, bisque limbs. Condition: generally excellent. Comments: Germany, circa 1870, the early dollhouse model is wearing her original multi-layered folklore costume from the Danish seacoast island of Amager. $200/300

62. *Early Furnished Kitchen with Original Painted Furnishings Known as "Holstensk Kokken"*

49"w. x 17"h. x 21"w. A wooden-framed two room kitchen comprises the cooking room and the pantry or breakfast room, has original painted blue/white patterned wainscot, black and white checkered floor, and original furnishings, viz. 18"w. hanging plate rack, corner cupboard with two paneled doors, another corner cupboard with 2 doors, 3 drawers and set-back shelves with shaped edging, 14"w. cupboard with 2 upper glass doors, 2 work tables, bench, slaughtering table, and faux-brick stove with built-in center chimney. Equipment and utensils include an unusual wooden figural boot scraper; 29 pieces of pewter or metal such as tankards, oil lamp, molds, milk

62.

62 detail.

62 detail.

cans, candlesticks, bowl, plates, and covered tureen; treenware such as Scandinavian ladle, bucket and plates, 16 pieces of copper pots, pans, molds, tea kettle, wooden-handled steamer; other utensils such as iron cleaner with ornately shaped upper edge, funnel, tongs, slaw cutter, 8-mold muffin pan, 3 porcelain jugs, various pattern glass including kettle and covered sugar and butter dishes. The early kitchen is named "Holstensk Kokken, Tyskland" (Holstensk Kitchen), Germany, circa 1875. $4500/6500

62 details.

63, 64.

65.

66.

63. German Cloth Character Doll by Kathe Kruse

14" (36 cm.) All cloth doll has pressed and oil painted facial features and brown hair, sculpted ears, shaded green eyes, pouty expression, muslin body with stitch-jointing at shoulders and disc-jointed legs, wearing original blue cotton suspender shorts, white linen shirt, socks and shoes. Condition: generally excellent, few paint rubs, arms dusty. Comments: Kathe Kruse, circa 1935, the doll has original stamp on feet bottom; the expression is most endearing. $800/1200

64. German Wooden Toys in Original Boxes

3" (8 cm.) 8" x 4" box, 3" doll. A pair of shaved wooden boxes with lids each contain a set of chip-carved wooden toys, one with lady, three sheep, fence and tree; the other with woman, three geese, fence and tree. Each figure has its original paint and is preserved, unplayed with, in its original box. Circa 1890. $400/500

65. German All-Bisque Miniature Boy with Hobby Horse

4" (10 cm.) All-bisque character boy with very plump face, sculpted blonde hair, painted facial features, pin-jointed bisque arms and legs, painted white stockings, blue shoes, is wearing a blue knit suit under an orange felt jacket, and is carrying a tiny paper mache toy hobby horse. Condition: generally excellent. Comments: Germany, circa 1900, the facial expression is most unusual and appealing, the hobby horse is rare with original paint. $300/400

66. Pair, German All-Bisque Miniature Dolls in Original Costumes

4" (10 cm.) Each is all-bisque with swivel head, brown glass eyes, closed mouth, peg-jointed bisque arms and legs with painted stockings and black flat shoes. Condition: girl has tiny chips at shoulders and reglue to right stringing loop; boy has small flake on torso at the neck. Marks: 10 31. Comments: Germany, circa 1900, the dolls have original blonde mohair wigs and wear their original matching flannel costumes. $400/500

67. Collection of Miniature Kitchen Utensils

7" (18 cm.) 7" egg poacher. Early wooden, metal and brass kitchen utensils for toy kitchen or stove, includes wooden handled

67.

68.

tin egg poacher, wooden utensil rack with five utensils, wooden salt tub, brass grater, pig-shaped cutting board, wooden-handled brass warmer, rolling pin, tongs, hammer, iron and iron trivet, and wire folding plate rack. Excellent condition. Germany, late 19th century. $500/800

68. *Doll's Antique School Work and Miniature Scrapbooks*

3" (8 cm.) Included are two maple wood pencil cases (largest 3") with sliding lids and decoupage decorations, with tiny pencils, along with knitted school bag filled with little notebooks with simplistic hand-drawn wild-flowers, and another school bag made by a child in simple cross-stitch needlework (unfinished on one side) and filled with seven miniature notebooks, including a wonderful scrapbook with tiny hand-tinted and cut-out vignettes. Very good condition. Mid-to-late 19th century. $200/400

69.

69. *German Cloth Character by Kathe Kruse*

14" (36 cm.) All cloth doll has pressed and oil painted facial features and softly shaded brown hair, painted brown eyes and shaded eye liner, closed mouth with pouty expression, muslin body with separately stitched thumbs, disc-jointed legs, stitch-jointed arms, nicely costumed in cotton striped dress, dotted Swiss pinafore, Dutch style cap, one piece undergarment, stockings, flannel slippers. Condition: generally excellent. Marks: Kathe Kruse (feet). Comments: Kathe Kruse, circa 1925, a rare model with very expressive features enhanced by fine original patina. $1100/1500

70. *Cast Iron Miniature Scale with Gargoyle Design*

6" (15 cm.)

The cast iron scale in original green paint has ornate base with figural gargoyles at each end, and original brass plates. Circa 1885. Excellent condition. $300/500

71.

72.

71. *Pair, Early German Bisque Dolls with Sculpted Hair in Original Costumes*

8" (20 cm.) Each has bisque shoulder head with pale complexion, blonde sculpted hair waved away from face and held by painted hair ribbon, modeled ears, painted facial features, blushed cheeks, original muslin stitch-jointed body, bisque lower limbs, painted black boots. Condition: generally excellent. Comments: Germany, circa 1875, the dolls wear their original matching gowns with wide lace trim, undergarments. $700/1100

72. *Early German Bisque Lady with Blonde Sculpted Hair in Rare Ornate Coiffure*

25" (64 cm.) Pale bisque shoulder head of adult lady with slender face and elongated throat, blonde sculpted hair waved across forehead and arranged in formal curls and decorated with a gilded hair bow, exposed ears, painted facial features with deeply set socket eyes, closed mouth, kid fashion body with shapely torso. Condition: generally excellent. Comments: Germany, circa 1875, the doll has regal size, elegant stature, rare coiffure, and wears an early morning gown with fitted back and full front. $700/1200

73. *Mid-19th Century Danish Faux-Half-Timbered Town House Known as "Fruens Vilje"*

26"h. x 26"w. x 13"d. An unusual wooden doll house with half-timber exterior architecture that is a miniature representation of the 18th/19th century historic homes. The narrow house with elaborate and high roof lines is painted cream with green painted timbers, red painted shingles, and has an unusual combination of both painted and cut-out windows; the painted windows are artistically shaded to appear as though snow has piled against the windows. There is a double-window dormer on the upper roof with cut-out window panes and a window box. A painted single dormer window is on each side of the lower roof line. Fancy gingerbread trim edges the entire roof line. The house has three rooms, each with original electricity, and original wall and floor paper or paint. The blue and red kitchen paint matches the wooden furnishings. The parlor wainscot is of pressed cardboard. The furniture includes five piece paint decorated kitchen set with faux grandfather clock; kitchen cupboard, stove, 3 signed (illegible) balloon back chairs, walnut Empire sofa, Maerklin style parlor stove, bedroom dresser, desk and table, towel bar and 4 chairs. Accessories include 5 Gottschalk potted flowers, soft silver metal display case and accessories, various oil lamps, wooden kitchen rack and utensils, and various dishes. There are 7 antique bisque dollhouse dolls. An exceptional dollhouse of distinguished architectural lines enhanced by artistic painted detail, mid-19th century. $7500/9500

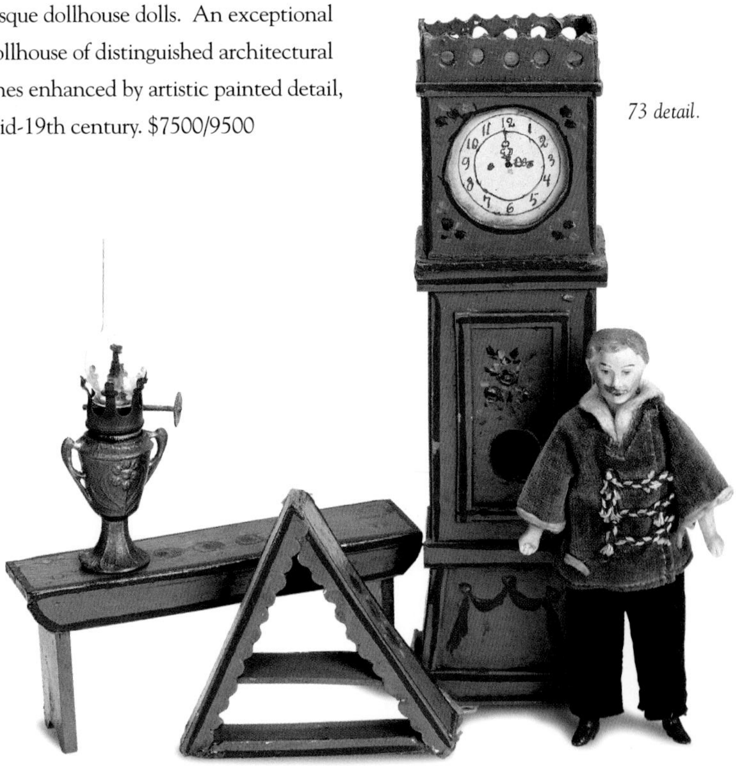

73 detail.

73.

73 details.

74. *Ensemble, Dollhouse Painted Cottage Style Bedroom with All-Bisque Doll*

4" (10 cm.) 4" doll, 6" bedroom set. The wooden bedroom furniture with cigar box backing on dresser is commercially made, with original painted cream finish and painted decorative roses and leaves, comprising cottage style dresser with mirror, washstand, night table, and bed with original fittings. Included is an all-bisque doll with jointed arms and legs, painted facial features, and antique costume. Excellent condition. Circa 1890. $400/600

75. *Set, Early Stencilled Parlor Furniture*

4" (10 cm.) In diminutive size, the dollhouse wooden parlor set has mahogany finish with gold stencilled geometric designs, the upholstered pieces with mauve velvet cover and gilded paper edging; comprising upright piano with keyboard lid, library table, round pedestal table, sofa, and set of six Gothic style dining chairs. Excellent condition. Circa 1870. $400/500

75.

76. *German All-Bisque Doll in Original Costume with Trunk of Toys*

4" (10 cm.) All-bisque doll with brown glass eyes, painted facial features, blonde mohair wig, jointed bisque arms, painted shoes and socks, is wearing factory original flannel jacket and pants, and is presented along with orange paper lithographed miniature trunk with lift-out tray, and having three miniature toys: all bisque clown with painted costume and jointed limbs, all-bisque Harlequin with painted costume and jointed limbs, and all-bisque tiny doll with original folklore costume. Excellent condition, clown with one broken hand. Germany, circa 1900. $400/600

77. *German All-Bisque Doll with Toy Rocking Horse*

5" (13 cm.) All-bisque doll with swivel head, cobalt blue glass eyes, painted lashes and brows, closed mouth, blonde mohair wig, jointed arms and legs, painted shoes and socks, antique knit costume. Marks: 2. Condition: tiny chip at neck of back torso and leg stringing hole. Comments: Germany, circa 1890, the doll has wonderful expression, included is early paper mache rocking horse with painted saddle and harness. $300/400

81.

79.

80.

78. *German Porcelain Doll in Antique Baby Buggy*

4" (10 cm.) 4" doll, 8"l. buggy. An all porcelain baby of the type known as "Frozen Charlotte" has painted hair and facial features, and is wearing an antique gown and bonnet; the doll is presented in a woven carriage with wooden hand grip, metal spoked wheels, and original leather sunshade and cover. Condition: generally excellent. Comments: Germany, circa 1885, an endearing arrangement in well-preserved condition. $400/600

79. *Miniature Doll Accessories*

4" (10 cm.) 4" ivory yarn winder. Carved ivory or bone yarn winder with elaborate detail is designed for screw-on firm attachment to a table or flat surface while the spinning cage below remains in motion. Along with a 2" bone-handled brass magnifying glass with excellent quality glass, and a miniature ABC book with various alphabet styles, dated 1849. Excellent condition. Mid-19th century. $400/600

80. *Miniature Bone Accessories and Blue Porcelain Dishes*

1" (3 cm.) A fine lot comprising a cherry wooden tray upon which are arranged a number of dollhouse sized ivory or bone accessories, viz. opera glasses, mouse cage, decorative box, and sewing accessories such as awl, darning egg, and sewing attachment. Also included is a partial porcelain dinner service in diminutive size (4" l. largest tray) with cobalt blue and gold trim, comprising serving tray, gravy boat, square bowl, round bowl, four shallow soup bowls, covered tureen and a large round serving dish. Excellent condition, chip on rim of one bowl. Germany/France, circa 1885. $500/900

81. *German Bisque Doll with Blonde Sculpted Hair and Blue Granite Kitchenware*

18" (46 cm.) Bisque shoulder head with short blonde sculpted hair in tousled curls, painted facial features, partially exposed ears, chubby features, kid body with gusset jointing, bisque forearms, antique costume. Condition: generally excellent. Comments: Germany, circa 1885, included are various blue granite ware kitchen pots, pans, sieve, strainer, ladle, roasting pan and more. $500/700

82 detail.

82. *Early 20th Century Furnished Doll House Known as "Villa Ellen"*

32"w. x 24"h. x 20"d. (including railing). The six-room wooden house with steeped roof has original grey paint with slate grey roof and trim. There are side windows on the ground floor, ten windows at the front; each window has painted panes on the outside and wooden panes on the inside. There is a double-hinged front door on each floor that center-opens to the balcony with balustrade on the second floor and to a large porch with fancy balustrade and hinged gate on the first floor. A hole at the roof peak appears to have a missing ornament such as a flag holder. The house is electrified with 4 hanging chandeliers, doorways between each room with a closing door into the kitchen. The painted walls and floors have old, possibly original, finish. There are lace curtains at all windows. The kitchen offers a built-in hanging cupboard and 2 shelves. Furnishings include kitchen work table, 8-piece ensemble of lime green parlor furniture including an unusual settee with bookcase top and silk upholstery, 4 piece of Biedermeier furniture, oak furniture including cupboard, 2 chairs, table and settee with red silk furniture, 2 maple single beds with matching marble top stands, two washings (one is a candy container), and a Maerklin style parlor stove. Accessories include blue granite ware, oil lamp, porcelain canisters with labels, bird cage, clocks, miniature photographs, opera glasses with Stanhope image labeled "Bismarck", lamps, candlesticks, and soft silver metal pieces such as hat rack, tea table, magazine rack and jardinière. There are four bisque dollhouse dolls. A well-furnished country villa of the early 20th century, of commercial although unidentified production, likely Germany, named "Villa Ellen" in homage to its original owner. $4500/6500

83. *Rare German Bisque Portrait Lady with Outlined Necklace*

25" (64 cm.) Pale bisque shoulder head of adult woman with black sculpted hair in very ornate fashion with rows and rows of arranged horizontal curls, sculpted blue hair band with gilt edging, painted facial features, pierced ears, blue painted necklace with outlined brooch having applied paper lithograph, muslin feedsack body, muslin

82 details.

83.

limbs, antique costume. Condition: generally excellent. Comments: Germany, circa 1870, the actual doll is shown in *German Doll Encyclopedia* by Cieslik, page 234, identified as a portrait model of the French Empress Eugenie. $700/1000

84. *German Bisque Doll Head with Blonde Sculpted Hair*

5" (13 cm.) Bisque shoulder head, a matching model of #83, except in smaller size, without the painted necklace and brooch, and having pale blonde hair. Condition: generally excellent. Comments: Germany, circa 1870. $300/400

84.

85. *French Bisque Poupee in Original Silk Folklore Costume*

15" (38 cm.) Bisque swivel head on kid-edged bisque shoulder plate, blue enamel eyes with spiral threading, painted facial features, closed mouth, pierced ears, brunette mohair wig, cork pate, French kid body with shapely torso and limbs. Condition: generally excellent, tiniest pinflake on right eye rim. Marks: 2. Comments: Gaultier, circa 1870, the poupee is wearing her original elaborate folklore costume with silk apron and headdress, padded bodice, velvet trimmed skirt, undergarments, shoes. $2000/2500

86. *Petite French Bisque Poupee with Unusual Body Style*

9" (23 cm.) Bisque swivel head on kid-edged bisque shoulder plate, pale blue glass enamel eyes, closed mouth, painted facial features, blonde mohair wig, wire upper arms and legs, bisque forearms, paper mache lower legs. Condition: generally excellent. Comments: Gaultier, circa 1885. Value Points: the petite lady is wearing delightful Normandy silk folklore costume and carries a basket of flowers. $600/900

87. *French Bisque Poupee by Jumeau in Antique Costume*

14" (36 cm.) Bisque swivel head on kid-edged bisque shoulder plate, blue glass paperweight inset eyes, painted facial features, closed mouth, brunette mohair wig, cork pate, kid gusset-jointed fashion body. Condition: generally excellent. Marks: 1 (head) Jumeau Medaille d'Or Paris (body). Comments: Jumeau, circa 1880, the petite lady wears her antique silk and velvet costume with violet trimmed bonnet. $1700/2300

88. *19th Century Dance Book with Carved Ivory Scene*

4" (10 cm.) A celluloid bound dance book with silk lining and attached ivory pencil, has surmounted ivory cover with elaborately carved scene featuring a young lad and lady dancing around a pole, sheep at their side. Excellent condition. $300/400

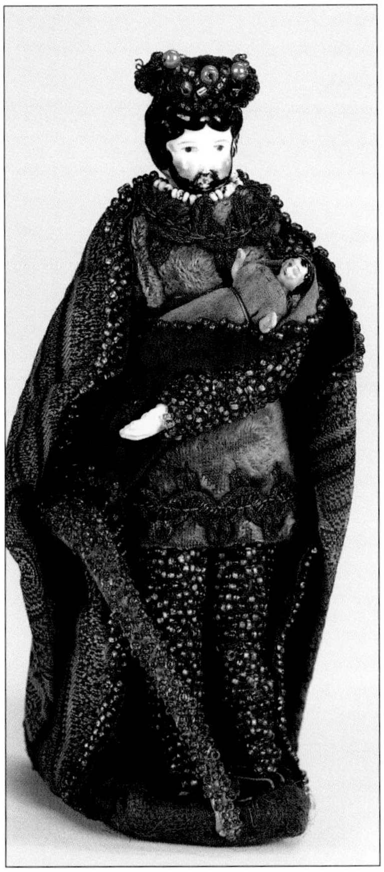

89.

89. *German Porcelain Dollhouse Man in Original Medieval Costume with Child*

6" (15 cm.) Porcelain shoulder head with black sculpted hair and painted beard and moustache, muslin body, porcelain limbs, wearing original beaded costumed and "jeweled" crown, holding tiny all-porcelain baby. Excellent condition. Germany, circa 1890. $300/400

90. *French Bisque Poupee by Jumeau*

17" (43 cm.) Bisque swivel head on kid-edged bisque shoulder plate, cobalt blue glass enamel inset eyes, painted facial features, closed mouth, pierced ears, blonde mohair wig over cork pate, muslin stitch-jointed body, leather arms, antique (worn) gown. Condition: bisque excellent, body worn and not original. Comments: Jumeau, circa 1875, the doll has beautiful face, fine antique bonnet and leather shoes, embroidered undergarments. $800/1200

91. *French Bisque Poupee with Brevete Neck Attachment*

17" (43 cm.) Pale bisque swivel head with flat-cut neck socket and unique attachment to original shoulder plate, cobalt blue glass enamel inset eyes, painted facial features, closed mouth, blonde mohair wig, kid gusset jointed fashion body, lovely antique white muslin gown, antique undergarments, slippers. Condition: generally excellent. Comments: from the original Brevete of Blampoix, circa 1865, the doll has rare neck system, beautiful eyes. $1700/2500

90.

91.

92. *German Wooden Dollhouse Gazebo with All-Bisque Dolls*

8" (20 cm.) A wooden framed gazebo with arched entrance doorway decorated with garlands of Spring flowers is enhanced with two German all-bisque dolls, each with swivel head, glass eyes, closed mouth, mohair wig, jointed limbs with painted stockings and shoes, and factory original knit costumes. Marks: 31 10 (dolls). Condition: gazebo excellent, brunette excellent, blonde has hairline and restoration to right foot. Comments: probably Paul Hunger, Germany, circa 1913, see Cieslik's *Lexicon des Puppenstuben* under Puppenhauser (page 105), a most appealing dollhouse accessory, also included is additional fencing of a similar style. $800/1000

93.

93. *Three French All-Bisque Miniatures*

2.5" (6 cm.) Each is all-bisque with solid dome, swivel head, painted features, peg-jointed bisque arms and legs, painted black ankle boots, blonde mohair wig. Condition: generally excellent. Comments: for the French market, circa 1890, the dolls wear matching original school children costumes of maroon flannel wool. $300/400

94.

94. *German All-Bisque Doll on Swing with Playmate*

8" (20 cm.) swing. A wooden-framed swing with original green paint holds an all-bisque doll with blue glass eyes, open mouth, jointed limbs, wearing cotton school dress, and standing nearby is a 4 1/2" bisque doll with blue eyes, open mouth, blonde mohair wig, five piece paper mache body, wearing knit sweater with matching pants and cap. Condition: generally excellent. Marks: GK 44.17 (body) 12 31 (girl). Comments: Germany, circa 1900. $400/600

95. *German Bisque Doll with Fancy Shoes*

7.5" (19 cm.) Bisque swivel head with plump face, brown glass inset eyes, painted facial features, closed mouth, blonde mohair wig, composition torso, bisque arms and legs, five-strap painted ankle boots with blue painted sides and little heels. Condition: generally excellent, composition torso may not be original. Marks: G.K. (head). Comments: Gebruder Kuhnlenz, circa 1890, a very appealing face, rare boots, and wearing original sateen costume, cap, and lace-edged cotton undergarments. $300/500

96. *German All Bisque Miniature Doll with Yellow Stockings*

4.5" (11 cm.) Bisque swivel head on kid-edged bisque torso, brown glass inset eyes, closed mouth, painted facial features, blonde mohair wig, jointed bisque arms and legs, painted yellow high stockings, black two strap shoes, antique costume. Condition: generally excellent, faint hairline on right thigh, right stringing loop rebuilt (inside leg). Comments: Germany, circa 1890. $200/300

97. *German All-Bisque Miniature Doll Attributed to Simon and Halbig*

6" (15 cm.) Bisque swivel head on kid-edged bisque torso, brown glass sleep eyes, painted facial features, closed mouth, blonde mohair wig, peg-jointed bisque arms and legs, painted white stockings with black two-strap heeled shoes. Condition: generally excellent, tiny flakes at front torso neck and left stringing hole of arm. Comments: attributed to Simon and Halbig, circa 1890, a pretty swivel head doll wearing antique dress and undergarments. $400/500

98.

98. *Two German All-Bisque Dolls with Garden Accessories and Carriage*

4" (10 cm.) Each all-bisque doll has swivel head, blue glass inset eyes, painted facial features, closed mouth, original blonde mohair wig, jointed limbs, painted shoes and stockings and wearing dainty lace or silk party dress. Condition: generally excellent. Marks: 31-10 (head and arms). Comments: Germany, circa 1890, included with the swivel-head dolls is a tin carriage with two tiny frozen Charlotte dolls marked "made in Germany", pine folding garden furniture comprising table, bench, four chairs, two wooden trellises with flowers, and two wooden pots with original flowers. $700/900

95.

96.

97.

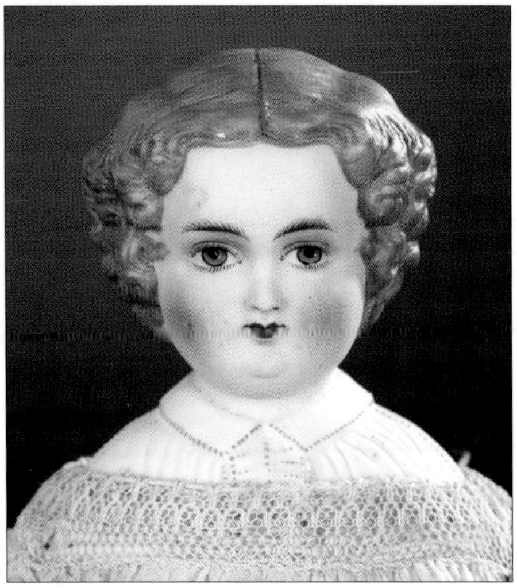

99. *German Bisque Lady with Sculpted Brown Curly Hair*

11" (28 cm.) Bisque shoulder head with rounded facial modeling, sculpted short curly brown hair, painted blue eyes with painted lashes and rose blushed eye shadow, closed mouth, original muslin stitch-jointed body with bisque lower arms, nicely costumed in antique clothing, leather shoes. Condition: generally excellent. Comments: Germany, circa 1885, unusual painting of facial features especially at eyes, rare brown hair. $400/500

100. *German Porcelain Lady with Fancy Coiffure*

12" (30 cm.) Porcelain shoulder head with black painted hair waved away from face and arranged in upswept fashion with braid at the chignon crest, stippling detail around the face, painted facial features, muslin body with bisque lower arms. Condition: generally excellent. Comments: Germany, circa 1875. $300/500

101. *German Porcelain Lady with Chignon in Petite Size*

9" (23 cm.) Porcelain shoulder head with rounded facial modeling, black painted hair in center part combed smoothly over the ears

102.

and into coiled chignon at back of head, painted facial features, muslin stitch-jointed body, leather arms, nicely costumed in silk gown, undergarments, lace bonnet, kid shoes. Condition: generally excellent. Comments: Germany, circa 1865. $300/400

102. *Early Danish Doll House with Furnishings Known as "Mormors Hus"*

40"h. x 38"w x 19"d. The large wooden red-painted house has black painted steepled roof with step-shaped roof line at the

100, 101.

102 detail.

edges and 2 center chimneys. There are two windows at each side and 8 arched windows at the front. The front hinges open at the center for access to the house. The interior features four large square rooms with connecting doorways having curtains, paper and paint of some age but may not be original; there is a hand-painted paper panel at the back wall. Three rooms have ceiling fixtures. The contents include fireplace, a petite Biedermeier ensemble featuring four cabinet pieces and sofa and 4 chairs, early maple bedroom ensemble with canopy bed and Gothic style chairs, rare painted tin buffet, chest and table, wooden dry sink and work table, cast iron stove, and four ladder back rush seat chairs. Accessories include a fine decoupage folding screen, metal cradle, sewing basket, bird cage, candleholders, pewter tray and dishes, blown glass dishes, "wishbone" chair, blue kitchen enamelware, blue and white canisters mortar and pestle, utensil racks, mantel clock, mirror with sconce, brass coal scuttle, and two unusual gesso medallions depicting Rousseau and Daniel McDowell Esquire. Two early bisque dolls with sculpted hair live in the house. The house is known as "Mormors Hus" (Grandmother's House), Denmark, circa 1870, and had originally belonged to the grandmother of Estrid Faurholt (see introduction). $6000/9500

102 details.

102 details.

103, 104, 105.

106.

103. *German Wax over Paper Mache Doll in Original Black Velvet Dress*

15" (38 cm.) Wax over paper mache shoulder head with blue glass enamel inset eyes, painted facial features, closed mouth with hint of smile, original brunette mohair wig in arranged coiffure with ribbon, muslin body, original paper mache limbs with fancy painted blue ankle boots with gilt edging. Condition: very good, unplayed with, typical complexion fading, small split on bottom front of breastplate. Comments: Germany, circa 1875, the doll wears her wonderful original black velvet and ivory silk gown. $400/500

104. *German Wax over Paper Mache Lady Doll with Fine Original Maroon Fashion Ensemble*

17" (43 cm.) Wax over paper mache shoulder head with rounded facial shape, brown glass sleep eyes, painted facial features, closed mouth, blonde mohair fleeced wig in tight curls, original muslin body with paper mache limbs, painted white stockings and mauve ankle boots with maroon upper stripes. Condition: generally excellent. Comments: Germany, circa 1885, fine unplayed with condition with sweet expression, fabulous antique black velvet and maroon silk fashion gown (silk blown on sash) with lace trim, matching bonnet, watch, fob and beaded bracelet. $500/800

105. *German Wax over Paper Mache Fashion Lady in Original Evening Gown*

14" (36 cm.) Wax over paper mache shoulder head, blue glass inset eyes, painted facial features, closed mouth, brunette mohair original wig, muslin body with paper mache lower limbs. Condition: typical age crazing on wax. Comments: Germany, circa 1875, the doll wears her original low-bodice silk evening gown generously trimmed with beaded decorations, beaded slippers, undergarments. $300/400

106. *German Bisque Dollhouse Gentleman in 18th Century Style Costume*

6" (15 cm.) Bisque shoulder head with brown sculpted hair in long sideburns, painted facial features, muslin body, bisque lower limbs. Condition: generally excellent. Comments: Germany, circa 1890, the gentleman wears his factory original fitted flannel jacket and vest with gilt paper edging, brown pants fitted inside knee-high boots. $300/400

107.

107. *Rare German Glass-Eyed Dollhouse Man as Troubadour*

6" (15 cm.) Bisque shoulder head with painted brown hair, sculpted moustache and goatee, brown glass inset eyes, closed mouth, muslin body, bisque lower limbs. Condition: generally excellent. Comments: Germany, circa 1890, the rare dollhouse model has glass eyes, goatee, and wears his original silk Shakespearean style troubadour costume and carries mandolin. $500/700

108.

108. *German Bisque Dollhouse Character in Original Costume*

6" (15 cm.) Bisque shoulder head with grey centerparted hair in chignon, painted facial features depicting an aged woman with prominent nose, semi-smile with beaded teeth, incised age wrinkles, muslin body, bisque lower limbs. Condition: generally excellent. Comments: Germany, circa 1890, the doll wears an unusual linen tunic and red cape. $300/400

109.

109. *German Dollhouse Furnishings Known as "Biedermeier" with Dollhouse Lady*

4" (10 cm.) 4" doll. The wooden dollhouse furnishings are decorated with gilt stenciled ebony lithographed paper to suggest rich woods, including hall mirror with marble shelf, bed with rose silk bed covers, toilette table with etagere back, wash stand with drawer, and recamier with royal purple silk upholstery. Included is a bisque shoulder head doll portraying an adult lady with exquisitely detailed face and blonde hair arranged in curls with blue bow at the forehead, muslin body, bisque lower limbs, antique costume. Condition: generally excellent. Comments: Germany, circa 1880. $600/900

110. *Six Gilded Ormolu Dollhouse Accessories*

1.5" (4 cm.) Six gilded ormolu accessories include fancy telephone, fruit dish with figural support, cruet holder (missing bottles), unusual hanging plant holder with side hooks, mirror on stand, and pedestal table with beaded rim and bird perch with a parrot on a chain. Excellent condition. Germany, circa 1890. $400/700

111 detail.

111. 19th Century Richly Furnished Cabinet House

32"h x 22"w x 9"d. A nicely shaped pinewood cabinet with 6-pane double glass doors that open at the center, features 5 interior rooms on 3 floors, including kitchen with separate dining area, parlor, dining room, bedroom and an upstairs sitting room. The furnishings include 15 pieces of Biedermeier furniture such as hall mirror, very fine cherrywood buffet with metal filigree trim, brass corner étagère, superb handmade petit point carpet, pair of gilt ormolu candle holders, and two Maerklin type stoves. There are 3 ceiling fixtures and a large number of fine decorative accessories and kitchenware, as well as five early dollhouse dolls. Circa 1885. $6000/8000

111 detail.

111 detail.

112.

112. German Bisque Doll with Sculpted Blonde Hair and Glass Eyes

15" (38 cm.) Bisque shoulder head with short blonde curly sculpted hair, blue glass inset eyes, painted facial features, closed mouth, muslin stitch-jointed body, bisque lower arms, stitched-on black boots. Condition: generally excellent, right thumb reglued. Comments: Germany, circa 1885, the doll wears beautiful antique white pique coat dress with embroidered capelet collar, undergarments. $400/500

113.

113. German Bisque Fashion Doll with Closed Mouth by Kling

14" (36 cm.) Solid domed bisque shoulder head, brown glass inset eyes, painted lashes, closed mouth, blonde mohair wig, muslin stitch-jointed body, bisque forearms. Condition: generally excellent. Marks: 123-5. Comments: Kling, circa 1880, the closed mouth fashion lady wears her original woolen plaid dress, undergarments, silk bonnet. $600/800

116. Petite French Porcelain Doll with Original Kid Body

8" (20 cm.) Pink tinted porcelain shoulder head with painted short black hair in boyish fashion, painted facial features, shapely kid body with tiny waist, one piece shapely legs, mitten hands. Condition: generally excellent. Comments: French, circa 1865, a rare model with fine hand pressed detail, original body. $400/500

114. Petite French Bisque Poupee by Jumeau

11" (28 cm.) Pale bisque shoulder head, cobalt blue glass enamel eyes, painted facial features, closed mouth, blonde mohair wig, kid fashion body with shapely torso, one piece arms and legs, mitten hands. Condition: generally excellent, body very clean and sturdy. Marks: Jumeau Medaille d'Or Paris (blue stamp on torso). Comments: Emile Jumeau, circa 1878, included with the rare small size poupee is her original silk and velvet gown, undergarments. $1100/1700

115. Two Sets of English Miniature Silver Tea Services

3" (8 cm.) 3" diameter round tray. Included is ribbed pattern tea service with lidded teapot, sugar and creamer, arranged on original wooden based tray with silver openwork sides; and 5" x 1" long double-handled tray with beautifully shaped coffee and tea pots on three curved legs, matching creamer, sugar bowl. Each piece is hallmarked or sterling marked. English, 19th century. $400/600

117. Two German Porcelain Miniature Inkwells

2" (5 cm.) 2"w. smaller. Each porcelain inkwell has colorful decorative flowers, carrying handle, and small receptacles for ink and drying powder. Germany, circa 1880. Excellent condition, original firing line on handle of larger. $300/500

118. Pair, German Porcelain Dollhouse Gentleman and Lady

6.5" (17 cm.) The lady and gentleman each has porcelain shoulder head with short black sculpted hair, painted facial features, muslin body, bisque lower limbs. Condition: generally excellent. Comments: Germany, circa 1870, the gentleman wears antique riding outfit with unusual leather pants, fitted shirt, and the lady wears white muslin gown with two little dolls attached to sash. $400/700

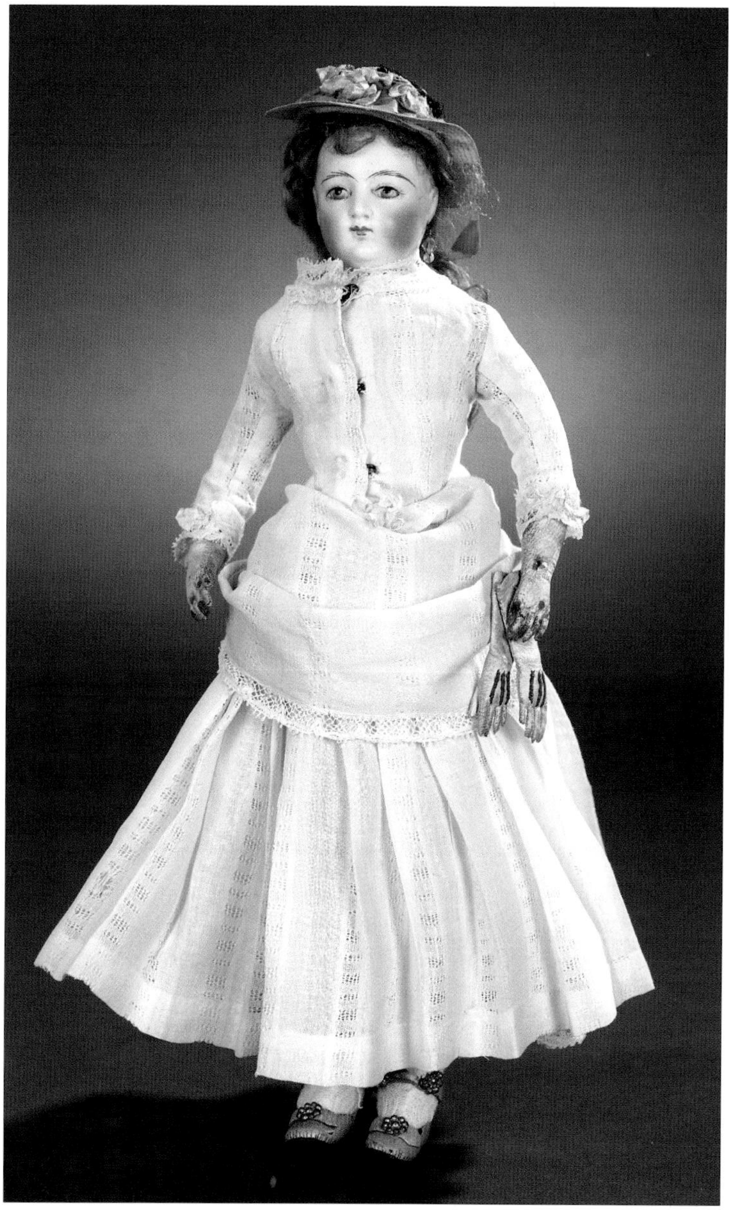

119. Miniature Porcelain Dresden Furniture with Cherub Decorations

3" (8 cm.) Five piece porcelain set of parlor furniture in an elaborate Victorian style with transfer designs of frolicking cherubs on each, along with applied pastel Dresden flowers and leaves and gilt stenciled outlines. Condition: very good, some typical chips on Dresden appliques. Comments: circa 1890. $300/400

120. French Bisque Poupee with Original Gown

13" (33 cm.) Bisque shoulder head with painted facial features, rich blue eyes, closed mouth with pert smile, blonde mohair wig, pierced ears, kid fashion body with shapely waist and legs, separated fingers. Condition: generally excellent, some finger spotting from internal wire. Comments: Barrois, circa 1865, the doll wears her original white fashion dress with lovely couturier detail, antique bonnet, undergarments, slippers, one earring. $1100/1500

121. *Beautiful German Bisque Doll in Original Folklore Costume of Isle of Amager*

15" (38 cm.) Bisque shoulder head with short blonde sculpted curly hair, painted facial features, blue eyes, solemn expression, muslin stitch-jointed body, leather arms. Condition: generally excellent. Comments: Germany, circa 1880, an especially sweet-faced model with rosy cheeks wears her original folklore costume from the Danish island of Amager including elaborate coiffe. $600/900

122. *Early Furnished Danish Dollhouse Known as "Tordis Hus"*

35"h x 37"w x 16"d. A two story wooden house with faux-brick paint, full-height faux-stone coigning at each corner, steepled roof with center chimney, four front casement windows, and 4 side windows, features beautiful paneled double doors at each front floor; the 1st floor door is protected by a columned pediment with the painted name "Tordis", and the 2nd floor doors are fronted by a circular shaped balcony with metal balustrade. There is one small ceiling light in each room, old (but possibly not original) paper and paint on the walls and floors of the four interior rooms, and lace and silk curtains at the windows. The furnishings include cherrywood pier mirror, Biedermeier pieces such as game table, pedestal table, 5 chairs, marbletop washstand, cupboard, washstand with fancy backsplash and bed, 2 walnut pedestals, other walnut furnishings comprising table, recamier, footstool and 2 chairs. Accessories include a fireplace with metal garniture and candles, music stand, 2 alabaster pedestals with bisque busts, towel bar, clock under dome, ormolu pedestal table, wooden kitchen rack with wooden plates, copper bed warmer, wooden dishes and more. There are four bisque dolls "living" in the home. From the early collection of Estrid Faurholt before its acquisition by the Lego Foundation Museum, the home was described in the 1965 book *A History of Doll Houses* by Jacobs, page 232. Danish, circa 1875, the home is named "Tordis" indicating the name of its original 19th century owner. $6500/9500

122 details.

122 details.

123.

124.

125.

126.

123. German Black Haired Porcelain Lady with Pierced Ears

15" (38 cm.) Porcelain shoulder head with slender face and elongated throat, black sculpted hair elaborately arranged with curls onto the forehead and nape of neck, pierced ears, painted facial features, early handmade cloth body, porcelain lower arms, paper mache lower legs, antique fashion gown, undergarments, earrings. Comments: Germany, circa 1870. $300/500

124. Three German Porcelain Dollhouse Dolls

6" (15 cm.) 6" two largest, each with porcelain shoulder head, black sculpted hair, and painted facial features. The large with red panel dress has smoothly drawn coiffure with chignon, (newer) wooden articulated body and porcelain limbs, antique gown; the small doll with ringlet curls and antique silk dress has (newer) wooden articulated body and porcelain limbs; and the larger doll in black velvet has original wooden body with porcelain limbs (left foot restored). Condition: excellent except as noted above. Comments: Germany, circa 1860, each with beautiful early face. $400/500

125. German Porcelain Dollhouse Doll with Wooden Articulated Body

5" (13 cm.) Thick paste porcelain shoulder head with pink tinting, black sculpted hair looped over the ears and falling into ringlet curls onto shoulders, painted facial features, wooden articulated body with shapely waist, dowel-jointing at shoulders, elbows, hips and knees, porcelain lower limbs, painted shoes. Condition: generally excellent. Comments: Germany, circa 1850. $400/600

127.

129.

126. *German Porcelain Dollhouse Lady in Antique Black Costume*

7" (18 cm.) Bisque shoulder head of adult woman with slender face, black sculpted hair, painted facial features, muslin body, bisque lower limbs, wearing an antique gown with black lace blouse, apron and cap, patterned skirt, undergarments. Condition: generally excellent. Comments: Germany, circa 1875. $200/400

127. *German Wooden Dollhouse Settee with Four Dolls*

4" (10 cm.) A tall oak settee features a mirrored and cubicle back above a silk upholstered seat upon which are seated two dollhouse ladies with porcelain heads, black painted hair and facial features, muslin bodies, bisque lower limbs, antique costumes. Also included is a porcelain man with short black hair, muslin body, antique brown velvet costume and unusual pink ankle boots, and a 3" bisque dollhouse boy with painted hair and features, wearing a blue antique suit, seated in metal rocking chair. Circa 1885. $300/400

128.

128. *German Porcelain Miniature Doll with Parlor Furniture and Tea Set*

6" (15 cm.) Porcelain shoulder head with black painted hair and facial features, muslin body, porcelain limbs, nicely costumed, along with an ebony painted wooden parlor set with unusual velvet patterned upholstery and tea table, comprising settee and three chairs. Also included is a smaller doll's doll, and a porcelain tea service with gold handles. Germany, circa 1890. Excellent condition. $400/500

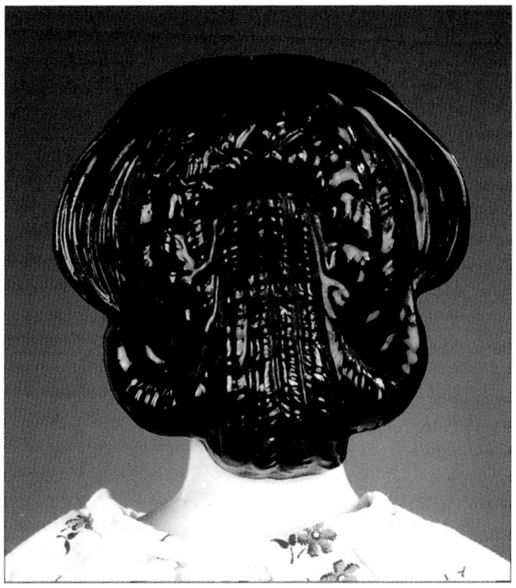

129 detail.

129. *German Porcelain Lady Doll with Rare Coiffure*

21" (53 cm.) Porcelain shoulder head of very slender adult lady with elegant elongated throat, black sculpted hair softly waved away from face into an elaborate arrangement of three rolled braids above a cascade of tight ringlet curls rolled under at the nape, painted facial features, blue eyes, muslin body, porcelain lower limbs with well sculpted hands and bare feet, antique hand-stitched gown, undergarments, tiny reticule. Condition: head excellent, body sturdy, right arm and leg restored, chip on left big toe. Comments: Germany, circa 1870, a rare model with exquisite sculpting. $800/1000

129.1

130.

131.

129.1. German Wooden Dollhouse Furnishings attributed to Wagner & Sohn

6" (15 cm.) 6" doll. A collection of wooden furnishings in the style referred to as Biedermeier, has rich dark finish with gold stenciled designs; included are bookcase with glass door top containing some miniature faux books, desk with elaborate cubicles and niches, hanging cupboard with mirror front, round pedestal table with rare accordion top, and game table with checkerboard top. Condition: generally excellent. Comments: Germany, circa 1880, attributed to Wagner & Sohn; included is a German black haired china doll with antique costume. $800/1000

130. Three German Tin Dollhouse Parlor Stoves

5" (13 cm.) Each of pressed tinplate, two having embossed brick designs and fretwork decorations, and two having brass doors and trim. Very good to excellent condition. Germany, circa 1890, possibly Maerklin. $300/500

131. Group of Soft Metal Dollhouse Accessories

3" (8 cm.) Each is of soft metal with gilded or silver finish, including 3" hanging mirror with attached swinging candlestick, hanging clock with movable pendulum, mantel clock with figural cherub, hanging oil lamp with milk glass shade (bottom amber glass broken), pair of candlesticks, and two three-arm candle holders. Excellent condition, except as noted. Germany, circa 1900. $300/500

132. *Group of Carved Ivory or Bone Miniature Accessories*

4" (10 cm.) 4" etagere. Each of minutely carved bone or ivory with fretwork details and attached accessories to the furniture, included is maple folding tea table with carved tray, candlesticks, two cups and saucers, and brush; sewing table with drawer that contains faux-sewing tools, round lidded jar with a large number of tiny pieces, and corner etagere with silk lined cabinet and three shelves of tiny dishes. Excellent condition. French/German, circa 1890. $700/900

133. *Superb Carved Bone Miniature Etagere*

2" (5 cm.) Very delicate carved bone display stand or etagere has unusual curved bone frame and three graduated size shelves containing tiny bone vases and dishes, along with a larger oval bowl on the top shelf with tinted fruit; the etagere is natural color with dark brown tinted edging. Excellent condition, dome included. $400/600

134. *Group of Dollhouse Colored Blown Glass*

2" (5 cm.) 2" epergne, 11 pieces. The superb miniature blown glass pieces include clear glass epergne, swirled decanter and glass, very rare amethyst and clear glass candlesticks, red-beaded clear decanter with stopper and glass, rose glass sherbet dish with pewter base, blue and rose candlestick with finger holder, and blue and swirled rose glass handled basket. Excellent condition. Circa 1900. $300/400

135. *Group of Rare Dollhouse Accessories*

2.5" (6 cm.) 2.5" clock, six objects. Included are carved ivory figure in early window box with gilt paper edging, bone opera glasses, and four gilt ormolu pieces, viz. birdcage with parrot, mantel clock with richly embossed base surmounted by flute-playing cherub, shell-shaped compote with figural pedestal, and lithograph painting of country scene with fancy frame (store label on reverse). Excellent condition. Circa 1890. $400/600

132.

133.

134.

135.

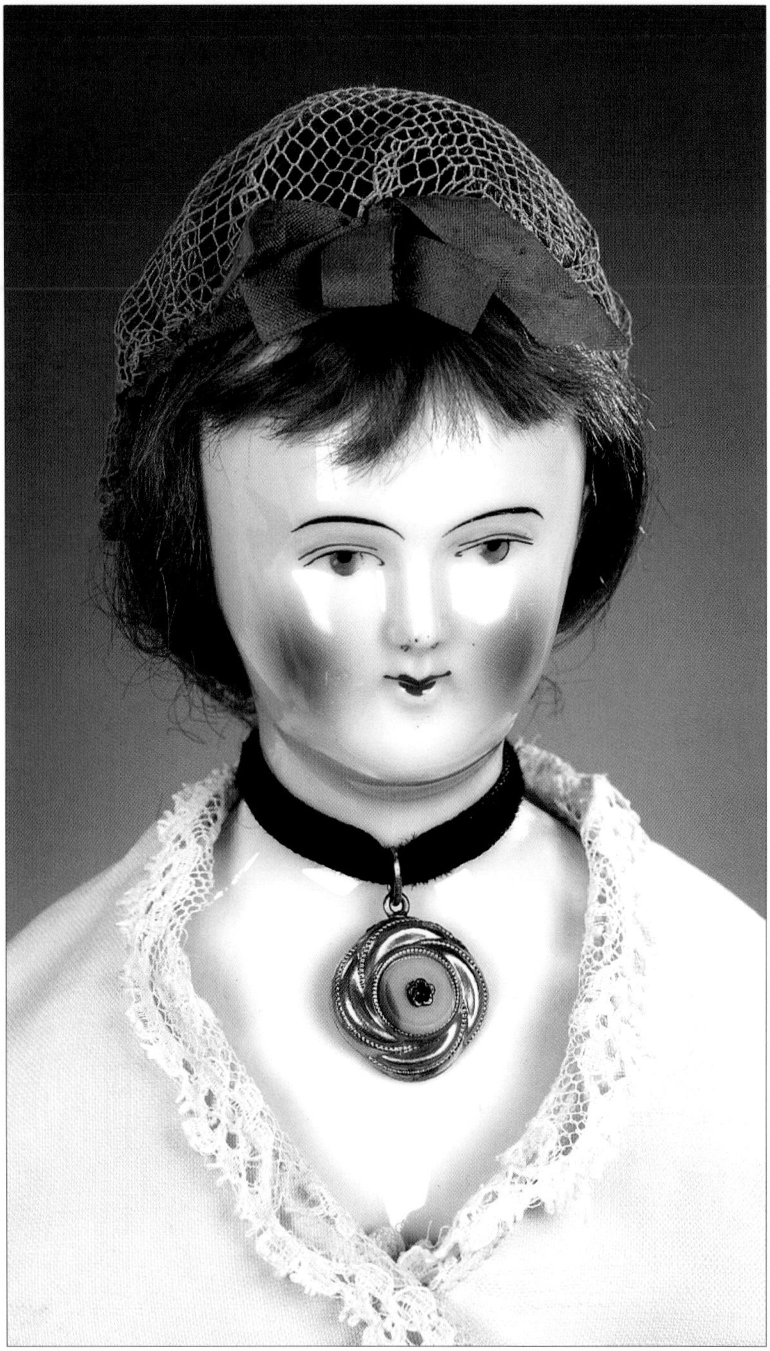

136. *German Porcelain Lady with Wig and Antique Costume*

21" (53 cm.) Solid domed porcelain shoulder head with painted facial features, elongated throat unusual for this model, brunette hair captured under woven snood, old kid body with shapely torso. Condition: generally excellent, body is charmingly too elongated for the doll, but the head and body have been together for many decades. Comments: Germany, circa 1875, the doll wears a fine antique two piece muslin gown, undergarments, leather high boots, richly gold-plated brooch. The doll was shown by Estrid Faurholt in her *Book of Dolls and Doll Houses* (1967), named "Charlotte" and described as having "funny old boots, not as smart as might be expected from the rest of her costume". $500/700

137 details.

137. *A Large and Well-furnished Three-Story House by Gottschalk*

40"h x 38"l. x 15"d. A large wooden house, painted cream with green trim, has an outset center that extends through both 1st and 2nd floors and terminates in a shaped arch at the attic roof that shades the set-back covered porch and is centered by small dormer windows on either side. The front opens in the center to reveal the house interior. There are cut windows at the front, an unusual fancy crest over the 1st floor portico and a four-angle red roof over the entire house. The left side of the house front has set-back porches with classic Gottschalk style lattice work and balcony railing, and there is a door into the house on each floor. The remainder of the front windows have fixed wooden shutters with painted designs, and there are metal hooks for window boxes on each window. The painted faux-windows on each side of the house are well executed. There are small hinged doors at each side of the attic, and the attic features three rooms. There are 5 rooms on the 1st and 2nd floor plus an entry foyer with hall closet and staircase to 2nd floor. The two center rooms have outset niches with windows at both the front and back of the house.

The furnishings include marble hall table, 4-piece woven rattan set, fancy oak armoire, grandfather clock, maple table with 5 chairs, maple furniture including rocking chair, sewing stand with tiny scissors, and 2 sofas (one marked by maker), gilded hall mirror, cast iron stove, wooden kitchen table with three chairs, paint-decorated kitchen cupboard with matching canisters, copper and brass parlor stove, 3 carpets, Biedermeier furniture including 3 balloon back chairs, 2 mini chairs, mirrored armoire, secretaire, and 2 sewing tables. Accessories include fireplace screen with decorative threadwork, 2 porcelain porch pots with feather plants, 2 hanging fixtures, pewter dishes, blue-green bucket, tin lantern, copper scuttle, glass blown bottles, Gottschalk plant pedestal, bisque bust on wooden pedestal, bone sewing basket, tiny woven basket, horn mirror, miniature Scandavian paintings dated 1901, and other various dishes. There are 9 antique bisque or china doll house dolls with antique costumes. The house is in original finish, original front steps included; there is typical wear and flaking to exterior finish, original wall paper and floors, original electrical ceiling fixture in each ceiling. The house appeared in the *1912 Catalog of Moritz Gottshalk* (see page 169 of Cieslik reprint of Gottschalk catalogs) and was considered a deluxe model. Circa 1912, Gottschalk. $9000/13,000

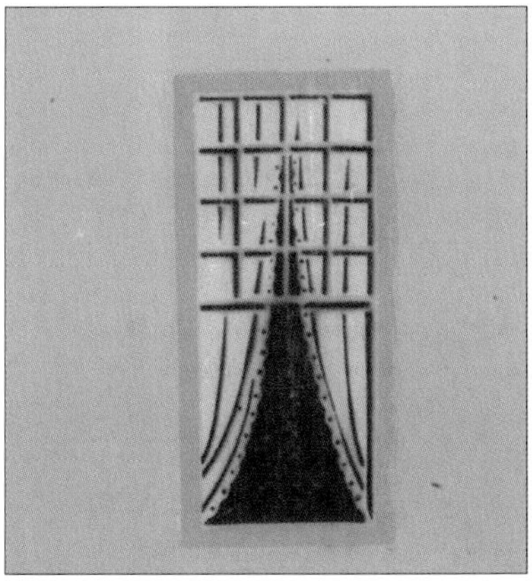

137 details.

138.

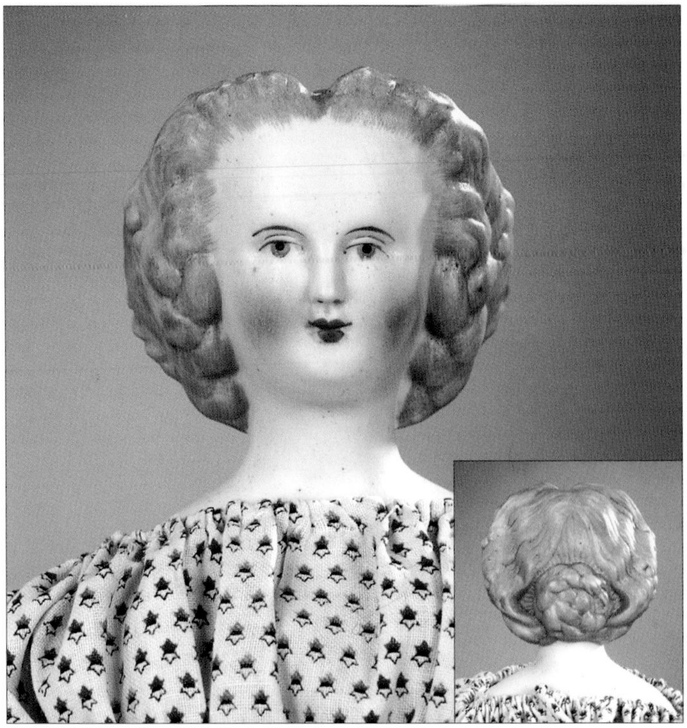

139.

140, 141.

138. *Lovely Petite German Bisque Fashion Lady with Sculpted Snood*

11" (28 cm.) Pale bisque shoulder head with elongated face and throat, blonde sculpted hair arranged in soft pageboy curls captured by sculpted snood and decorated with hair bows at either side of face (snood and bows same color as hair), painted facial features, blue eyes, old cloth body with wooden arms and legs, shapely waist. Condition: generally excellent. Comments: Germany, circa 1870, a beautiful doll with superbly sculpted hair, and original mauve patterned muslin gown, undergarments. $400/600

139. *German Bisque Lady with Brown Hair in Ornate Coiffure*

16" (41 cm.) Pale bisque shoulder head with elongated throat, painted brown hair in center part waved away from face is soft curls and loosely woven braids, and brought to the back of the head into a loosely braided coil, painted facial features, blue eyes, muslin stitch-jointed body, bisque lower arms. Condition: generally excellent. Marks: 2X. Comments: Germany, circa 1875, rare hair color with very fine detail of sculpting, early cotton gown, undergarments, leather slippers. $400/500

140. *German Bisque Fashion Lady with Sculpted Blonde Hair*

13" (33 cm.) Bisque shoulder head of adult lady with long blonde sculpted hair in elaborate arrangement of curls at top of head, bangs, and arranged curls onto back shoulder plate held by a tiny narrow braid at the neck, painted facial features, large blue eyes, pierced ears, muslin body, bisque lower legs, nicely costumed in antique gown and undergarments. Condition: generally excellent, one cloth arm appears shorter. Marks: 10. Comments: Germany, circa 1875. $300/500

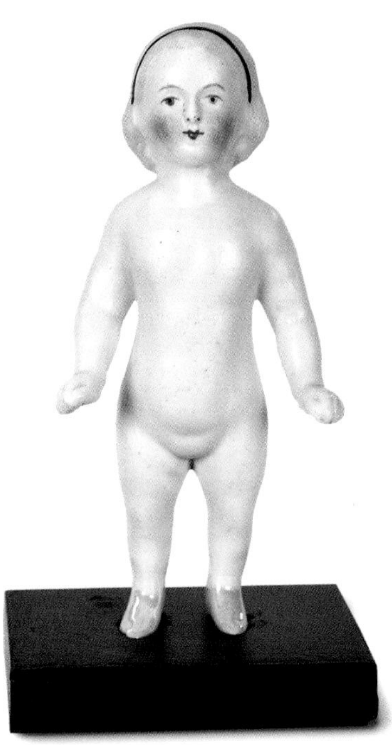

142.

141. *German Bisque Lady with Blonde Sculpted Hair and Black Hair Ribbon*

13" (33 cm.) Bisque shoulder head with blonde sculpted hair elaborately arranged with tight curls at the forehead and a black hair ribbon in front and behind a large rolled curl at the crest of the head, pierced ears, painted facial features, muslin body, porcelain limbs with painted flat black boots, antique delicately printed muslin gown, undergarments. Condition: generally excellent, tiny chip on right front toe. Comments: Germany, circa 1880. $300/500

144, 145.

142. *German All-Bisque with Black Hair Ribbon and Lustre Boots*

4.5" (11 cm.) One piece all-bisque figure of standing child, arms held forward and away from body, blonde sculpted hair waved from face into softly rolled pageboy curls, black hair ribbon tucked behind sculpted ears, painted facial features, unusual painted green lustre boots. Condition: generally excellent. Comments: Germany, circa 1865. $300/500

143.

143. *German Bisque Doll with Sculpted Hair Known as "Alice in Wonderland"*

10" (25 cm.) Pale bisque shoulder head with blonde sculpted hair waved away from face into softly rolled curls and held by black hair ribbon at the crest and behind the ears, painted facial features, muslin body, bisque lower limbs, painted black laced boots. Condition: generally excellent. Comments: Germany, circa 1880, the model is often referred to "Alice in Wonderland", the doll wears wonderful antique dress, undergarments. $400/500

144. *An Early German Pink Tinted Porcelain Baby*

9" (23 cm.) One piece pink-tinted porcelain standing baby with hand-pressed detail, blonde painted baby hair with stippling, painted facial features, well-defined character expression with chubby cheeks and sculpted ears, chubby baby rolls and dimples well defined on body. Condition: generally excellent. Comments: Germany, circa 1880. $400/600

145. *Rare German Porcelain Bonnet Baby with Original Body and Bunting*

5" (13 cm.) One piece porcelain head and upper torso, sculpted baby bonnet with ruffled edging and red painted ribbon, painted facial features, muslin torso with bellows, jointed porcelain arms, one piece porcelain lower torso and chubby legs. Condition: generally excellent. Comments: Germany, circa 1865, the rare taufling baby with sculpted bonnet and original costume has its original blue cotton printed bunting and sacque. $600/1000

146 details.

146 details.

146. English Wooden Pink House Known as "Clevendon Court" With Exceptional Interior Decorations

25"h. x 24"w. x 23"d. A large rectangular house with painted pink finish to suggest rose stone work has white cornerstones, red shingled roof with flat top, small hole at flat top of room, and four chimneys with 2 chimney pipes in each. The front and back walls are each removable for access to different rooms. The front features a front door with architectural portico and four front steps with railing, four paned windows at the second floor and two paned windows at the first floor. Inside are 2 rooms, each side flanking a large center foyer with elaborate staircases and banisters; there is inlay on the floor, back wall and below the stair banister, beading around the doors, Moorish themed decorations on the upper walls that matches decorations on two outside side windows, and 4 gesso decorations hanging on the marble papered walls; the wallpapers and floors are original. The back of the house features eight four-panel windows and four rooms; the two upstairs rooms have original marbled wallpaper. The downstairs room has a well-detailed fireplace with unique Chinese earthenware figures on the mantel in front of a painting, while another room has Chinese carved panels and fretwork arch decorated with bronze and silver architectural panel. Exquisitely detailed in its interior architecture, the house is unfurnished. English, late 19th century. $5000/7500

147 detail.

147. German Bisque Lady With Brown Sculpted Hair and Ruffled Dresden Collar

18" (46 cm.) Bisque shoulder head of adult woman with delicately tinted complexion, brown sculpted hair in elaborate coiffure with braid across the forehead decorated with Dresden rose and leaves, looped braids behind and below the ears with cascading finger curls, very fancy glazed Dresden ribbon-shaped ruffled and decorated collar, pierced ears, painted facial features, blue eyes, muslin stitch-jointed body, bisque forearms, antique costume. Condition: generally excellent, some chipping of rose and leaf petals. Comments: Germany, circa 1870, very rare and intricately sculpted lady doll. $800/1100

148.

150.

149.

152.

148. *Two German Bisque Dollhouse Dolls in Original Costumes*

7" (18 cm.) Each has bisque shoulder head with sculpted hair and painted facial features, muslin body, bisque forelimbs, including a brown haired lady with very fine Edwardian style costume and matching hat, and officer with black painted hair, brown eyes, moustache, and red and blue flannel officer's military uniform. Condition: generally excellent. Comments: Germany, circa 1900. $500/700

149. *Two German Bisque Dollhouse Dolls*

7" (18 cm.) Each has bisque shoulder head, painted facial features, muslin body, bisque forelimbs, including lady with brown mohair wig, jointed all-bisque arms, wearing ivory silk satin wedding gown with lace trim, and officer with brown sculpted hair, blue eyes, moustache, wearing red and blue flannel officer's uniform. Condition: generally excellent. Comments: Germany, circa 1900. $400/500

150. *French Bisque Poupee with Original Maison Giroux Label*

12" (30 cm.) Bisque swivel head on kid-edged bisque shoulder plate, cobalt blue glass enamel inset eyes, painted facial features, closed mouth, pierced ears, blonde mohair wig over cork pate, kid gusset-jointed fashion body, wearing red silk gown with black lace trim, bonnet, undergarments, tiny leather shoes. Condition: bisque excellent, body original albeit a bit weak. Marks: B 0 S. (head) Alph. Giroux 43 Boulv. des Capucines Paris (body). Comments: Blampoix, circa 1865, the petite poupee was sold by the luxury Paris store of Giroux. $1500/1800

151. *German Bisque Portrait Lady with Blue Hair Ribbon*

18" (46 cm.) Bisque shoulder head with blonde sculpted hair arranged with tiered rolled horizontal curls down the back of head and vertical rolled curls at the sides, a wide blue hair ribbon at the crown, painted facial features, pierced ears, unusual firmly-stuffed coarse twill body with wooden limbs, painted flat blue shoes. Condition: generally excellent, tiny chip at bottom corner of front shoulder plate. Comments: Germany, circa 1875, note the blue eyes and hair band color that matches exactly, the doll wears a fine antique brown and black silk fashion gown, undergarments. $500/800

152 details.

152. *English Dollhouse "The Brown House" with Stained Glass Windows*

30"h. x 27"w. x 27"d. A large wooden house of square proportions features a low roof with painted green shingles and a single chimney with eight stacks. The house is stained a rich dark brown and has well-defined quoining at each corner, and architectural window frames with wide sills, and windows that hinge open at the center and are topped by a rectangular glass window for extra light. One side features three large windows and a large reception door with carved panels below a painted faux-leaded window that is flanked by five smaller faux-leaded windows. Another side features four windows and a richly paneled door with brass lion's head door-knocker. The third side features four windows, and the rear of the house is solid excepting one single plain door that opens to a single room. The interior, only accessed by the windows and doors which may account for its remarkable originality, is fitted with exquisite early wallpaper throughout, and a full-length fireplace and mantel in the front hall. The house is unfurnished excepting the fireplace, and an early German engraving with cutwork and applied decoration, in original pressed gilt frame with German description describing a cheerful life. Excellent original condition. Probably English, circa 1840. $7000/11,000

153. *Group, Miniature Silver and Porcelain Accessories*

2" (5 cm.) 2" goblet. Included in the fine group is a silver goblet marked "L&S" with hallmarks; five beaded rim ruffled edge coin silver plates marked 830S, plated silver candlestick with finger hold, and three white porcelain pots or jug with cobalt blue decorations and plated silver handles, spout and lids. Excellent condition. Late 19th century. $400/600

154. *A Large and Well-Furnished 19th Century Dollhouse*

43"h x 43"w x 18"d. A large wooden house of simple design features eight front windows with beveled edge sills, hinged roof exposing a playroom and attic space, natural wood floors, old curtains and wallpapers. The house is richly furnished with elegant tall ceilings, hanging ceiling fixtures or chandeliers in each room, and fine furnishings including 9 pieces of Gottschalk furniture, various miscellaneous antique furnishings in the attic, children's and music room, fine maple wood dining room set including folding tea table, cupboard, dessert server, and excellent decorations including a little Christmas tree, plant holder with ferns, clock under dome, parlor stove, hanging clocks, and more. There are seven dollhouse dolls including 2 men with moustaches and a soldier and parlor maid; plus 3 babies. Late 19th century. $4000/6500

154 details.

154 details.

155. *German Bisque Fashion Lady with Closed Mouth*

23" (58 cm.) Bisque shoulder head turned to the right, brown glass sleep eyes, painted facial features, closed mouth, brunette human hair wig, muslin stitch-jointed commercial body, bisque lower limbs. Condition: generally excellent, 3 finger tips chipped. Marks: 10 L. Comments: Kestner, circa 1890, the doll wears an elegant two piece flannel plaid fashion gown, undergarments, sewn-on red stockings and leather slippers. $500/700

156. *German Bisque Closed Mouth Doll by Kestner in Petite Size*

14" (36 cm.) Bisque shoulder head turned to the right, brown glass inset eyes, painted facial features, closed mouth, brown human hair over plaster pate, commercial muslin body with bisque lower arms and legs, bare feet. Condition: generally excellent, right arm reglued at top. Marks: E. Comments: Kestner, circa 1885, very pretty child with rare body style, bisque bare feet, lovely antique costume. $400/500

157, 158.

159.

160.

157. *Beautiful French Bisque Poupee with Signed Jumeau Body*

19" (48 cm.) Bisque swivel head on kid-edged bisque shoulder plate, blue glass enamel inset eyes, painted facial features, closed mouth, pierced ears, blonde mohair wig over cork pate, French kid poupee body with gusset jointing. Condition: generally excellent, body very sturdy except one finger broken. Marks: 4 (head and shoulders) Jumeau Medaille d'Or Paris (torso). Comments: circa 1875, the lovely poupee with very sturdy signed body has antique undergarments, leather boots, and fine antique gown. $2500/3500

158. *Petite French Bisque Poupee, Size 1, by Gaultier*

14" (36 cm.) Bisque swivel head on kid-edged bisque shoulder plate, blue glass enamel inset eyes, closed mouth, painted facial features, blonde mohair wig over cork pate, French kid poupee body with shapely waist, separated fingers. Condition: generally excellent. Marks: 1 (head) F.G. (shoulder). Comments: Gaultier, circa 1880, the petite lady wears antique costume, undergarments, leather shoes, stockings. $1200/1700

159. *French Bisque Poupee with Cobalt Blue Eyes*

13" (33 cm.) Bisque swivel head on kid-edged bisque shoulder plate, cobalt blue glass eyes, painted facial features, closed mouth, ears pierced into head, brunette mohair wig over cork pate, kid gusset jointed fashion body, separated fingers, wearing detailed undergarments, (frail) antique green taffeta gown included, bonnet, stockings. Condition: faint hairline on forehead. Comments: Barrois, circa 1865. $1200/1500

160. *Rare Tiny Size French Bisque Poupee in Antique Costume*

10" (25 cm.) Bisque swivel head on kid-edged bisque shoulder plate, cobalt blue glass eyes, closed mouth, painted facial features, brunette mohair wig over cork pate, kid poupee body with shapely waist, wearing antique green and cream silk gown, straw bonnet, undergarments. Condition: generally excellent, body a bit weak at the waist. Comments: Barrois, circa 1865, a very rare tiny size to find. $1100/1500

161.

161. German Bisque Dollhouse Bride with Ornate Hall Mirror

5" (13 cm.) 5" doll. A bisque shoulder head doll with blonde sculpted hair and painted facial features, muslin body, bisque lower limbs, is wearing her very elaborate silk bridal gown with beaded tulle veil and long train. Along with a gilded pressed metal hall mirror with faux-marble top. Excellent condition. Circa 1880. $400/600

163.

162.

162. German Bisque Dollhouse Gentleman and Ormolu Settee

7" (18 cm.) Bisque shoulder head gentleman with black sculpted hair and moustache, painted facial features, muslin body, bisque lower limbs, painted black boots, wearing his factory-original evening suit, with paper label on the back "Leopold"; along with 6"l. gilded ormolu settee with fretwork border and maroon silk cover. Doll excellent, settee discolored at paper back. Germany, circa 1890. $400/500

163. French Bisque Poupee with Gesland Body by Gaultier

18" (46 cm.) Bisque swivel head on kid-edged bisque shoulder plate, blue glass enamel inset eyes, painted facial features, closed mouth, blonde mohair wig over cork pate, pierced ears, Gesland body from original Pannier patent with padded stockinette over metal armature, bisque hands and lower legs, bare bisque feet. Condition: generally excellent. Marks: 3 (head and limbs) F.G. (shoulderplate). Comments: Gaultier, circa 1875, with rare body style allowing infinite articulation, beautiful bisque limbs. $2500/3500

164. *Five German Porcelain Babies*

4.5" (11 cm.) Four are one piece porcelain figure of standing baby with arms held in front, painted curly black hair and facial features, one with sculpted bonnet, one with painted blue stocking ribbons; the fifth is a seated all-porcelain baby in faux-wood grain tub with one arm held to chest. Condition: one head reglued, bonnet baby has chips on feet front. Circa 1890. $200/300

165. *German All-Bisque Doll with Rare Miniature Table*

4" (10 cm.) All-bisque doll with swivel head, jointed limbs, brown glass eyes, closed mouth, blonde mohair wig, painted shoes and socks, antique sailor costume and cap, with early dollhouse table having cast iron rustic style base to simulate early log furniture, silver finish, walnut round table top. Condition: generally excellent. Marks: 31 10 (doll). Comments: Germany, doll circa 1900, table is likely earlier, also included are yellow blown glass vases and ruffled edge bowl. $400/600

166. *German All-Bisque Doll with Parlor Stove and Scuttle*

4" (10 cm.) All bisque doll with solid dome head and torso, cobalt blue glass eyes, closed mouth, painted facial features, blonde mohair wig, peg-jointed bisque arms and legs, painted white stockings and black heeled shoes, wearing antique folklore costume. Condition: generally excellent, tiny chip on left thigh. Comments: Germany, circa 1885, also included is Maerklin type embossed tin parlor stove and black metal coal scuttle with gilded handle. $300/400

167. *German All-Bisque Doll with Two Labeled Press Metal Chairs*

4" (10 cm.) All-bisque doll has swivel head, cobalt blue glass eyes, closed mouth, painted facial features, peg-jointed bisque arms and legs, painted white stockings and black shoes, blonde mohair wig, antique silk dress and undergarments. Condition: generally excellent, tiny chip at top of torso. Comments: Germany, circa 1900, also included are two rare pressed metal chairs with bronze finish having lift-up velvet covered seats, the chairs labeled "W. Avery & Sons No 617 Redditch". $300/500

168. *German Soft Metal Furniture and Dollhouse Lady*

4" (10 cm.) A set of early soft metal furniture features a filigree table top with original painted floral decoration, along with three matching chairs having faux-woven seats. Also included is a German bisque dollhouse lady doll with rare sculpted brown hair in waved back fashion with braided chignon at the back of head, muslin torso, bisque lower limbs, original costume. Condition: generally excellent. Comments: Germany, circa 1875, both the doll model and furniture are rare to find. $300/500

169. *German Tin Dollhouse Garden Furniture and Pair All-Bisque Dolls*

3.5" (9 cm.) Each all-bisque doll has swivel head, glass eyes, blonde mohair wig, jointed limbs, painted shoes and socks, lace party dress; also included is a set of unusual bent-wire garden furniture in original green paint with pierced tin yellow seats to simulate woven wicker. Excellent condition. Germany, circa 1900. $400/500

170. *German Miniature Christmas Tree and Two Dolls*

4.5" (11 cm.) A miniature feather tree with original attached candles and glass balls is arranged upon a green wooden tree stand. Included is a bisque dollhouse lady with blonde sculpted hair, painted facial features, muslin body, bisque limbs, wearing antique brown cotton print house coat, and an all-bisque baby with painted hair and facial features, jointed limbs, wearing original flannel coat and bonnet, posed in metal doll stroller. Excellent condition. Germany, circa 1890. $400/500

171. *German Bisque Dollhouse Lady with Desk, Candle and Book*

5.5" (14 cm.) Bisque shoulder head doll with blonde sculpted short curly hair, painted facial features, muslin body, bisque lower limbs, is wearing a lovely antique gown and undergarments. Included is a Wagner & Sohn wooden dollhouse desk with paper lithographed faux-wood cover and rich gilt decorations, upon which is resting a faux-ivory candlestick and a book "Pensees et Maxims" with thoughts by various philosophers. $500/800

172. *German Bisque Dollhouse Lady with Baby in Cradle*

6" (15 cm.) Solid domed bisque shoulder head with painted facial features, blonde mohair wig, muslin body, bisque lower limbs, fancy painted orange ankle boots, wearing peach silk dress and antique undergarments, along with a bent wire swinging cradle with canopy, outfitted with lace and silk bed linens, and containing a small all-bisque baby with jointed limbs. Excellent condition; Germany, circa 1885. $400/500

173. *German Painted Tin Miniature School Desk and Dollhouse Doll*

4" (10 cm.) Bisque shoulder head doll with blonde sculpted hair waved away from face and held by a black hair bow behind her sculpted ears, painted facial features, muslin body, bisque lower limbs, antique costume. Included is a rare painted tin school desk with attached bench in original and beautifully preserved finish. Germany, circa 1870. $400/500

174. *German Bisque Dollhouse Doll with Carriage and Dog*

4" (10 cm.) Bisque dollhouse doll with blonde sculpted hair and painted facial features, muslin body, bisque lower limbs, wearing lovely antique dress; along with metal filigree wide baby carriage containing two all-bisque miniature dolls with original knit costumes, and a bisque dog with well detailed sculpting. Excellent condition. Germany, circa 1890. $300/400

175. *German All-Bisque Nanny with Two Bisque Babies and Wicker Furnishings*

3.5" (9 cm.) All-bisque doll with solid head and torso, brown glass eyes, painted facial features, brown mohair wig, jointed limbs, unusual high yellow stockings and black shoes, wearing original Nanny costume including coiffe, carrying a tiny all-bisque baby with sculpted hair. Included is another all-bisque doll with blonde sculpted hair and painted shoes and socks, jointed limbs, posed in a woven wicker cradle with embroidered blanket, and a woven wicker hooded park chair with wooden seat. Excellent condition. Germany, circa 1900. $400/600

176. *Danish Miniature Antique Shop "Leif Kobmand"*

27"w. x 13"h. x 15"d. A stage-like wooden setting with window display at the right side has attached 16-drawer cabinet and shelving units at the back, carved crest with name of shop "Leib Kobmand" and word "Antik" lettered above shop window. The shop is lavishly crowded with miniature antique treasures, including a collection of antique dolls in the front window: all-bisque bride and groom, 2 tiny Frozen Charlottes, 3 other all-bisques including jester with molded hat, 3 bisque doll heads, and a blonde hair china. Other antiques include a fine early 3-figure framed silhouette, iron jumping horse and jockey, brass thermometer (working) with figural of woman, large wooden mirror on bracketed floor frame, hand-painted Asian tapestry, painting of a boat, ormolu table mirror, gilded oil lamp with figural base, tin lithographed lunch pail, 2 tin mantel clocks, wooden Scotch bottle with two die inside and screw-off lid, mini-photo in painted metal frame, bisque trinket box with molded hand under a dome, metal pendulum clock with mirror, birdcage and bird, various lithographs, porcelain and glass dishes and decorative objects, hats and hat box, 2 bisque doll heads, tin glove, various furniture including sewing desk with drawer, chairs, desk and pedestal with bust of military hero. There are two dollhouse people including blonde hair china lady, and a bisque dollhouse man with modeled hat. Circa 1900. $1500/2000

176 details.

177. *Large German Bisque Doll by Kling*

26" (66 cm.) Solid domed bisque shoulder head, blue glass inset eyes, painted facial features, closed mouth with wistful expression, commercial muslin body, bisque lower arms and hands, antique blonde human hair wig, lovely antique white wear dress, undergarments, leather boots. Condition: generally excellent, 2 finger tip chips, light nose rub. Marks: 167 12. Comments: Kling, circa 1890. $500/700

178. *German Bisque Character by Kestner with Velvet Dog*

12" (30 cm.) Bisque socket head, blue glass sleep eyes, painted facial features, open mouth, two porcelain teeth, brunette human hair wig, composition bent limb baby body, nicely costumed, especially nice original condition of body. Condition: generally excellent. Marks: F made in Germany 10 247 JDK. Comments: Kestner, circa 1915, known as "Baby Jean", the doll owns an early painted velvet seated dog with large glass eyes, possibly Steiff. $600/800

179. *German Bisque Brown-Eyed Character by K*R with Baby Rattle*

11" (28 cm.) Solid domed bisque socket head, painted baby hair and facial features, rarer brown eyes, composition bent limb baby body. Condition: generally excellent. Marks: 28 K*R 100. Comments: Kammer and Reinhardt, circa 1908, the doll has original body and body finish, beautiful bisque, and wears

178.

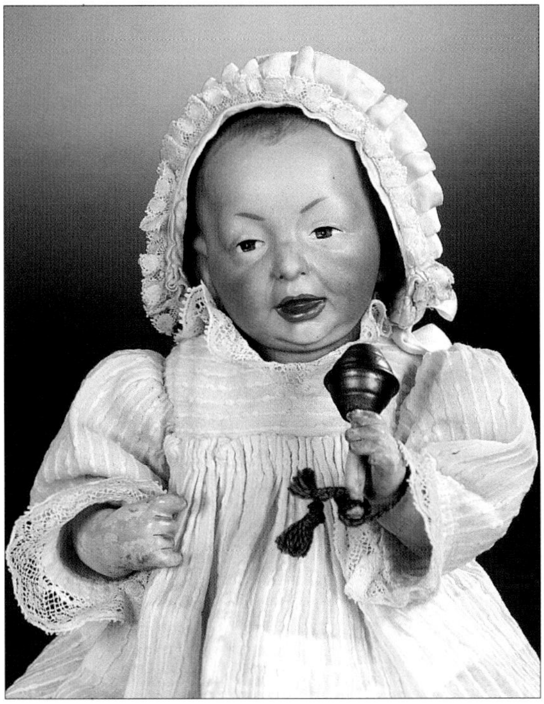

179.

its antique baby costume and bonnet, carries a bone-handled gilded baby rattle. $300/500

180. *German Bisque Closed Mouth Girl with Rare Bisque Feet*

12" (30 cm.) Solid domed bisque shoulder head, blue glass inset eyes, painted facial features, closed mouth, blonde mohair wig, muslin commercial body, bisque lower arms and legs, bisque bare feet, nicely costumed. Condition: generally excellent, light body patching, one tiny flake on underside of left middle finger. Marks: 2. Comments: probably Kling, circa 1885, the doll and her companion (#181) were featured in many of the Legoland Museum booklets. $400/500

180, 181.

181. *German Bisque Boy in Blue Velvet Sailor Suit by Kling*

12" (30 cm.) Solid domed bisque shoulder head, brown glass inset eyes, painted facial features, closed mouth, blonde mohair wig, muslin body, bisque lower arms and legs, bare bisque feet. Condition: hairline above right eye, lower right eye rim flake. Marks: 167 K (in bell). Comments: Kling, circa 1890, the shy-faced boy wears wonderful antique blue velvet sailor costume with matching cap, and along with #180 was featured in many photographs of the Legoland Museum. $400/500

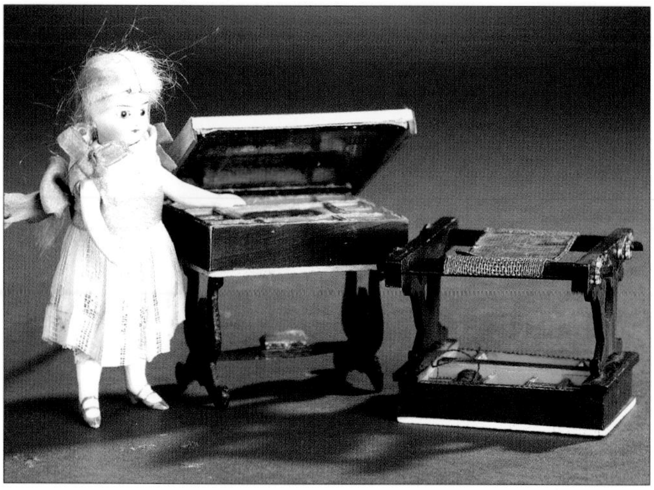

182, 183.

182. French All-Bisque Mignonette in Original Costume

4.5" (11 cm.) Bisque swivel head on kid-edged bisque torso, cobalt blue glass eyes, closed mouth, painted facial features, blonde mohair wig, peg-jointed bisque arms and legs, painted white stockings, and bright blue two-strap shoes, wearing antique dress with blue silk ribbon trim. Condition: generally excellent. Comments: for the French market, circa 1885, most appealing pert expression. $400/600

183. Two German Dollhouse Furnishings

2.5" (6 cm.) Two needlework furniture pieces, each of wood with lithographed paper finish to simulate mahogany finish with stencilled gilt designs, commonly known as Biedermeier, includes a sewing table with fitted interior under the lift-up top (no contents) and unusual padded cushion on the under support; along with a very rare tapestry frame with original faux-tapestry and underside with fitted niches for various yarns. Very good condition, tip chipped on one foot of sewing table. Germany, likely Wagner & Sohn, circa 1875. $300/400

184.

185.

184. Four German Gilded Ormolu Dollhouse Pieces

5" (13 cm.) 5"h. dressing table. The ormolu pieces include a richly embossed dressing table with set-back storage having working drawer, below a fancily bracketed mirror; table with checkered top and cabriole legs; unusual spiral twist candle stick with finger hold; and table top clock with easel back. Excellent condition. Germany, circa 1890. $500/800

185. Fine Group of Miniature Silver Pieces

4" (10 cm.) 4" candlestand, 7 pieces. Included is candlestand with tripod pedestal base and revolving double candleholders, unmarked but likely sterling; silver urn with elaborate double handles and embossed designs on urn and base, unmarked but likely sterling; silver plated double-handled loving cup; silver candle holder with finger hold and beaded rim, and thimble-shaped bowl, neither marked but likely sterling; a book-shaped fancy trinket box with interior lid that contains baby's tooth, marked sterling; and an early silver three ball-footed cup with ball-tipped handle, hallmarks, whose lid is centered by a silver Danish coin dated 1689. Excellent condition. $600/900

186. 19th Century Music Box as Grand Piano with Dollhouse Marquis

5" (13 cm.) A wooden grand piano with painted and carved wooden keyboard has lift-top with support, and contains a lovely two-tune music box that operates from keywind on the underside; along

186.

187.

with bisque dollhouse man with blonde sculpted hair, painted facial features, muslin body, bisque limbs, wearing a silk and lace Marquis costume that appears factory original. Excellent condition. Circa 1880. $500/700

187. *German Dollhouse Ormolu Accessories and Glass Ceiling Lamp*

4" (10 cm.) 4" etagere, five pieces. Each of gilded ormolu including Art Nouveau style etagere with arched loop at the back and petal top front posts; ornate birdcage with wall attachment and colorful parrot; double-handled vase, wall bracket gas lamp with milk glass shade; and an unusual hanging ceiling fixture of milk glass with beaded and painted decorations, brass frame and chain attachments. Excellent condition. Germany, circa 1890. $600/900

188.

189.

188. *French All-Bisque Mignonette with Bare Feet and Original Costume*

5" (13 cm.) Bisque swivel head on kid-edged bisque torso, cobalt blue glass eyes, closed mouth, painted facial features, blonde mohair wig, cork pate, peg-jointed elongated bisque arms and legs, bare feet. Condition: generally excellent, tiny chip at bottom of neck socket. Comments: French, circa 1885, the doll wears her original fancy dress and bonnet. $900/1300

189. *French All-Bisque Mignonette with Painted Blue Shoes*

5" (13 cm.) Solid domed bisque swivel head on kid-edged bisque torso, cobalt blue glass eyes, painted facial features, closed mouth, blonde mohair wig, peg-jointed bisque arms and legs, painted white stockings and blue two-strap heeled shoes. Condition: generally excellent, left leg reglued above the knee. Comments: French, circa 1885, the pert-faced girl wears her original lace-edged muslin dress and pantalets, pressed felt bonnet with silk ribbons. $800/1000

190. *Very Rare Miniature Lithopane as Fernery*

6" (15 cm.) A sturdy metal two-tiered fernery, in original black paint with gilded fretwork railings and ball-tipped fancy edging centers a lithopane panel which, when held to the light, reveals a scene of a young girl training her puppy. Circa 1890. Excellent condition $600/900

191 detail.

191. *Large Wooden Dollhouse Kitchen with Center Attached Chimney*

30"w x 18" d x 16" h. A sturdy large wooden kitchen room in stage-like form has painted cream walls and checkerboard floor, attached painted green plate rack with red stenciled design that extends to all three walls and is centered by an attached chimney with green warming shelf. There is a window on the left wall and a door on the right, and a built-in sink and cupboards. A wooden stove with painted brick design is under the chimney and there is a large painted green cupboard with red stenciled and floral designs to match the plate racks. Other furnishings include a drop-leaf table, small chairs, and butcher block. Many accessories include wooden keg, tinplate kitchen utensils, molds and pots, scale, earthenware pots, porcelain dishes, pewter plates, and earthenware. Circa 1880. $2000/2500

192. *Pair, German Bisque Boy and Girl in Original Folklore Costumes*

7" (18 cm.) Each has bisque shoulder head with blonde sculpted hair, painted facial features, muslin body, bisque lower limbs. Condition: generally excellent. Comments: Germany, circa 1885, the dolls wear their original folklore costumes, the girl with padded bodice, woolen skirt, apron and woven basket carrying supplies, the boy with leather work apron, kidskin jacket, fitted leggings with red ties. $400/500

193. *German Porcelain Dollhouse Doll and Imangle*

5" (13 cm.) Porcelain shoulder head doll with short black curly hair, painted facial features, muslin body, bisque limbs, is wearing a multi-layered antique costume of beautifully printed fabrics, topped by red,

193.

white and blue striped apron, cap and sewing bag. Along with a soft-metal elaborately scrolled mangle in original painted colors of green, tan and red. Excellent condition, few paint flakes. Germany, circa 1885. $300/500

194. Four Miniature Wooden Boxes with Painted Decorations

1.5" (4 cm.) Four oval boxes, the largest 1 1/2"h., with 4" lid, each of bentwood except the smallest which is carved wood with elaborately carved design on the sides and a carved flower on the lid. The largest has varnished finish over red painted flowers with green leaves, carrying handle, and letter "ar 1906" on the side; the green painted box, 3"l. is decorated with delicately rendered flowers on the lid and leaf pattern on the sides; and the final box, undecorated, is topped with a paper mache piglet. Excellent condition. Late 19th century. $400/600

195. German Bisque Doll in Original Folklore Costume with Baby Bunting

11" (28 cm.) Bisque shoulder head with blonde sculpted short hair and bangs, brown glass inset eyes, painted facial features, muslin body, bisque lower arms and legs. Condition: generally excellent, tiny flake on hair. Marks: 131 2/0. Comments: Kling, circa 1885, the doll wears her original Scandanavian folklore costume with rich detail, antique leather shoes, and carries a bisque baby bound inside an unusual leather bunting, its little leather bound feet sticking out at one end. $300/500

195.

196. German Bisque Dollhouse Lady at Wash Day

6" (15 cm.) Bisque shoulder head with blonde sculpted hair, painted facial features, muslin body, bisque lower limbs, painted shoes, wearing original detailed folklore costume, marked 7/0. Condition: generally excellent. Comments: Germany, circa 1890, included with the doll is a wooden clothesline, woven wash basket with wooden clothespins, oval wash basket with towels, and an oval hooded cradle with little black celluloid seated baby. $300/400

194.

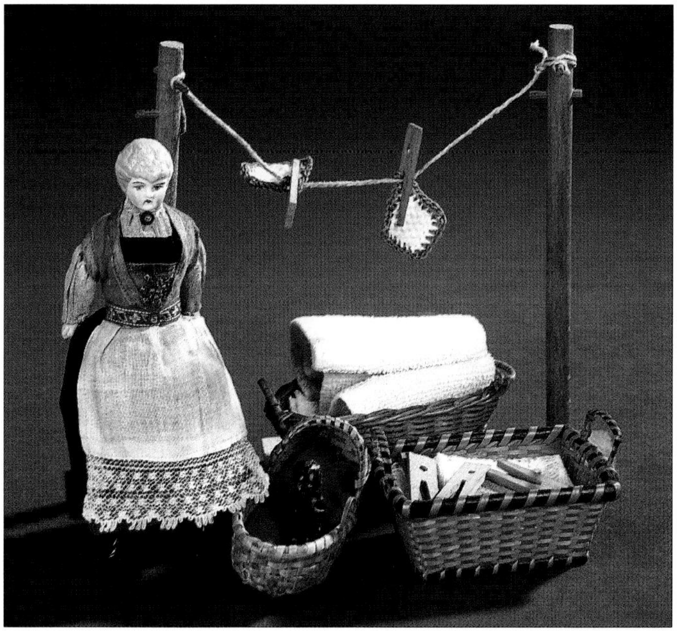

196.

197.

197. *Early Large Wooden House Known as "Skovgaarden"*

39"h x 30"w x 16"d. A large wooden two-story house has painted yellow brick façade with painted stone quoining and lintels that are artfully achieved with shaded effects. The roof has dark green painted shingles and there is a single dormer in the center of the roof. The house has 4 large windows with arched tops and a center double door with painted wood-grain finish and painted decorative window over the doors. The front hinges open for access to four large non-connecting rooms and the back roof hinges open for access to one large attic room. The rooms have replaced paper or painted walls and floor. The name "Skovgaarden", presumably the family name of the original child owner, is painted over the attic dormer window. Exterior is excellent with original well-preserved finish. Circa 1880. $6000/8000

198. *Group, German Wooden Miniature Kitchen Utensils*

3.5" (9 cm.) 3" coffee grinder, 8 items. Included is wooden coffee grinder with pewter top and handle, wooden tip; painted wooden sausage, two cutting boards, tin tray with lithographed designs,

197 detail.

198.

199 detail.

199.

wooden handled cleaver, wooden tray with cut-out handles, and an unusual wooden tub with original yellow paint, iron straps and handles. Excellent condition. Late 19th century. $300/400

199. Small Wooden Dollhouse Cottage Known as "Solvang"

24"w x 15"d x 21"h. The simple wooden cottage or caretaker's home is of thick wood with original ochre painted finish, having sloped green painted roof, double chimneys, center room dormer with two arched windows (one glass missing) and a railing for plants. The sides are solid wood, but the front features two faux-four-paned windows with wide flower sills that flank a center painted double door with paneled and glass window front (glass missing) and two front steps. The upper frames of the windows and front door are well defined as is the base of the roof. The house is open at the back to reveal a large single attic room and two 1st floor rooms with connecting doorway and painted finish. The name "Solvang" (sunny field) appears above the door in a defined name plate. Circa 1885. $2500/3500

200. Petite German Wax over Paper Mache Doll

10" (25 cm.) Wax over paper mache shoulder head with blonde sculpted hair waved away from face and captured by wide black hair band, black glass inset eyes, painted facial features, muslin body, wooden lower limbs, painted black flat boots. Condition: very good, typical craze lines at top of head. Comments: Germany, circa 1875, the appealing petite doll has original finish, original body,

and wears a finely detailed simple antique costume with beautifully detailed multi-layered undergarments. $200/400

201. Group, 19th Century Miniature Kitchenware

7" (18 cm.) 7"h. traveling set. Included is a heavy porcelain traveling set of three casseroles arranged in stacking fashion with one lid overall on tin and wooden handle; seven white enamelware plates; pressed tin lunch basket with handle and double-hinged lid; two iron skillets with white enamel interiors and aqua undersides (one for poaching), marked "303"; two double handle cast iron bowls and two skillets, each with white enamel interior, each marked "NAC&Co Morso"; and a larger shallow double-handled cast iron bowl marked "F" with crown mark. Very good to excellent condition, tin lunch pail a bit used, "303" skillets worn. Late 19th century. $400/600

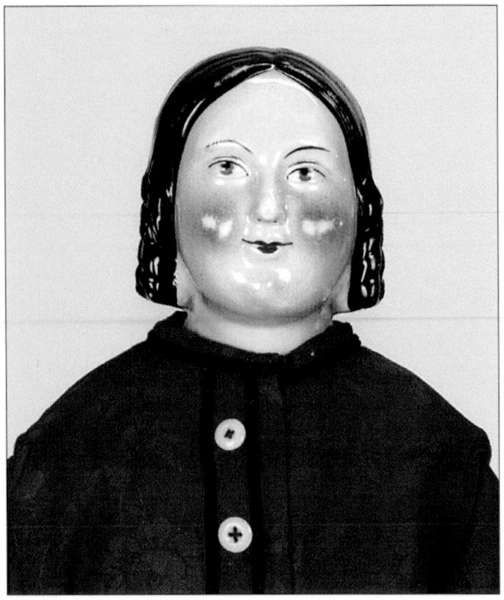

202.

202. *German Porcelain Lady with Wonderful Face*

21" (53 cm.) Thick paste pressed porcelain shoulder head with plump modeling and endearing smile, black sculpted hair in center part with short finger curls, painted facial features, deeply set eye sockets, muslin stitch-jointed body, leather arms, antique costume. Condition: back left corner of shoulder plate missing 1" piece, paint rubs on cheeks and hair. Comments: Germany, circa 1860, the doll has most endearing expression, and was highly featured in many of the Legoland Museum brochures. $400/500

203. *Large German Porcelain Doll with Hand-Pressed Detail*

25" (64 cm.) Thick paste porcelain shoulder head with plump face and shoulders, black sculpted hair waved away from face into soft pageboy curls and held by sculpted black hair ribbon, exposed ears, painted facial features, muslin body, paper mache arms to above the elbows, wearing wonderful antique woolen dress, undergarments, stockings, leather shoes, necklace, and carrying little toy ball. Condition: generally excellent. Comments: Germany, circa 1875, the same model as the modeled-hair bisque doll known as "Alice in Wonderland", here in porcelain with rare black hair for this model. $400/600

203.1. *Miniature Kitchen Accessories*

3" oil lamp. Included is wall-hanging porcelain utensil rack with four wood-handled utensils, wooden slaw cutter with built-in knife, tin oil lamp on wall bracket, wooden wall rack with lithographed tin names, and wooden tub with painted decorations. $400/500

204. *German Porcelain Doll in Labeled English Costume, with Miniature Baskets*

9" (23 cm.) Porcelain shoulder head with black sculpted hair, painted facial features, muslin body, bisque lower limbs. Condition: generally excellent. Marks: A & G.E. Grace, High St. House Guernsey (paper label on back of skirt). Comments: Germany, circa 1890, the English milk maid wears her original labeled costume, carries a tin bucket, her knitting, and owns four antique woven baskets in delightful miniscule patterns. $300/500

205. *German Porcelain Doll in Original Danish Folklore Costume*

15" (38 cm.) Porcelain shoulder head with black sculpted hair waved behind the modeled and pierced ears into chignon at back of head with curls tumbling onto the neck back, sculpted bangs, painted facial features, muslin stitch-jointed body, porcelain hands. Condition: generally excellent, finger tips on right hand chipped. Comments: Germany, circa 1885, the doll is wearing her authentic and well-detailed Danish folklore costume with embroidery and elaborate red wooden trimmed coiffe. $400/500

206. *Early 20th Century Miniature School room with Five Bisque Dolls*

5" (13 cm.) 5" dolls. Each doll has bisque head, painted or glass eyes, five piece paper mache body, original simple cotton school dress, marked "Germany". Included are three wooden school desks with attached benches having inkwells, pencil holders, and book shelf; globe on wooden pedestal stand, abacus, and four small slate boards. Excellent condition. Circa 1900. $600/900

207. *Early and Rare Earthenware Cistern with Faucet, and German Doll*

9" (23 cm.) German bisque shoulder head doll with blonde mohair wig, painted facial features, pierced ears, muslin body, bisque lower limbs, wearing her original country costume. Condition: generally excellent, crack at rear of cistern. Comments: Germany, circa 1880, included with the doll is a rare earthenware cistern with sculpted cherubic design, working silver faucet, and removable lid. $300/500

208. *German Miniature School Room with 8 Students*

10"h. x 20"w. x 14"d. A stage-like wooden setting with rear glass double window, and original paper and floor paper depicts a school room, with four double school desks with attached benches, teacher's desk with lift-up table top, inkwell and bell, 2 blackboards, heating stove and coal bucket. Other accessories include 5 school bags and hats hanging on the wall hooks, tin clock, lithographed wall maps, abacus, tin globe on wooden pedestal, and workbooks for each student. There is a bisque head teacher with modeled hair, and 8 all-bisque dolls with jointed limbs, 2 having painted eyes and 6 with glass eyes, in antique school costumes. Circa 1900. $900/1300

209 detail.

209. *German Miniature Furnished Dining Room*

10"h. x 12"w. x 9.5"d. A stage-like wooden setting featuring two large curtained windows at the rear presents a turn-of-the-century dining room of a bourgeois family, having papered walls and paper lithographed faux-wood floor. The dining room furniture is of matched oak wood with silk upholstery on the chairs and includes table, 3 side chairs, 1 armchair, straight-back sofa with silk upholstery and attached high shelf, and a table and cabinet with mirrors. There are 2 painted metal flower stands, an iron stove and coal bucket, wooden corner étagère, and various accessories, viz. gilded soft metal serving cart with wheels, large gilded metal oil lamp with milk glass shade, glass fruit bowl, silver-lidded glass stein, silver book box, pewter plates, framed lithographs, and an embroidered area rug. A black haired china woman and little girl people the house. Circa 1890. $1000/1500

210 detail.

210.

210. *German Miniature Sitting Room with Gilded Furnishings*

9.5"h. x 14.5"w. x 9"d. A charming small wooden room in stage like setting with decorative side columns and a large glass curtained window at the back has lithographed wall paper with decorative border, and lithographed-paper floor in parquet design. The room is furnished with gilded or silvered soft metal pieces comprising of a fainting couch with pale rose silk upholstery, matching foot stool, circular table, plant rack, side table, 2 fancy chairs, 2 benches, miniature table with mirror and a tall mirror with shelf. There is an embroidered rug, and accessories including an unusual bird perch, 3 framed lithographs of women, framed lithographed of horse, and several large vases. There is an all-bisque jointed doll included. Germany, circa 1890. $1200/1700

211 *German Miniature Lady's Sitting Room*

9"h. x 18"w. x 9"d. A petite wooden room in stage-like setting features decorative side columns and two back curtained windows with wooden valences, papered walls and floor. The room is furnished with a black bentwood ensemble comprising tea table with 4 chairs having upholstered seats, matching loveseat, rocking chair and foot stool. There is an unusual carved bone toiletry table, and a tin flower stand with attached birdcage with bird. A pair of oval framed silhouettes hang on the wall, and a blonde haired china doll stands in attendance. Germany, circa 1900. $1200/1500

211.

212. *French Paper Mache Poupee with Early Costume*

16" (41 cm.) Solid domed paper mache head with painted black pate, very angular face with elongated throat, painted facial features, closed mouth, tan cloth body that appears original. Condition: generally excellent, nose rub. Comments: for the French market, circa 1840, the lady wears an early silk print gown with lace trim, undergarments. $900/1200

213. *French Paper Mache Child Doll in Original Costume*

10" (25 cm.) Paper mache shoulder head with black painted pate and painted curls around the forehead, original slit cut for wig insertion, painted facial features, pink kid body with defined waist and leg muscles. Condition: generally excellent. Comments: for the French market, circa 1850, the doll wears wonderful original cotton print dress, apron with ruffled edge pocket, undergarments, leather slippers. $400/600

213.1. *Collection of Tin Kitchen Accessories*

4" scale. Included is embossed iron front scale, tin dust pan with stenciled children design, two wall-hanging canisters, sieve, oval tray and tea canister with lithographed designs. Excellent condition. Circa 1900. $300/400

214. *Set of 6 Quill and Feather Miniature Chairs*

5" (13 cm.) The frame of each chair is made of delicate bone quill held by tiniest brass tacks, with bird feather seats. Very good condition. Mid-19th century, the chairs are very rare. $300/500

215. Grodnertal Wooden Miniature Doll with Baby

5" (13 cm.) All wooden doll with painted back hair and facial features, paint-over-gesso complexion, dowel-jointed arms and legs. Condition: generally excellent. Comments: Grodnertal, circa 1850, the doll wears her original silk, lace and homespun costume and bonnet, and holds a tiny all-jointed Grodnertal baby. $400/500

216. Tiny Grodnertal Doll with Tinier Doll on Cushion

3" (8 cm.) All-wooden doll with painted black hair and facial features, paint-over-gesso complexion, very elongated throat, fully jointed wooden body, wearing antique costume. Condition: generally excellent. Comments: Grodnertal, circa 1840, included is a tiny 1 1/4" Grodnertal doll with painted tuck comb and fully jointed body, posed on a mauve velvet cushion. $300/500

217. Early Miniature French Engraving in Frame

2" (5 cm.) 2" x 2 1/4". An early delicately tinted engraving of the Paris Palais du Justice is arranged in its original gilt metal over wood frame with closing clips at the back, and an early lettered description of the Palais. Excellent condition. Circa 1840. $300/500

218. French Paper Mache Poupee with Glass Eyes

17" (43 cm.) Solid domed paper mache shoulder head, black enamel inset eyes, painted facial features, closed mouth, black painted pate under human hair wig, pink kid poupee body with shapely waist and legs, mitten hands. Condition: generally excellent, some paint rubs on lips and nose tip. Comments: for the French market, circa 1850, the doll wears a fine early dress of patterned cotton over chemisette, undergarments, lace bonnet, stockings, shoes. $800/1100

219 detail.

219. A Small Rustic Cottage with Curved Front Steps

14"h x 19"w x 12"d. A thick-wall wooden cottage with brown paper lithographed finish and painted black sloping roof features a paint-decorated front door flanked by columns with surmounting arched portico, and fronted by unusual gradual-width curving front steps. There are 2 floor-to-ceiling paned windows at the front and each side, two dormer windows in the roof, and a center chimney. The only access is through the front door and a hinged door in the rear roof. The one-room interior has old wall and floor paper and curtains. The house is unfurnished excepting a rug and two pictures. Structurally excellent, the brown paper finish is worn. Circa 1890. $2000/2500

220. Wooden Folk Art Carved Dollhouse Furniture with Bisque Doll

9" (23 cm.) Bisque shoulder head doll with elaborately sculpted blonde hair, painted facial features, muslin body, bisque lower limbs, painted black boots, is wearing her factory original knit folklore costume. Condition: generally excellent. Comments: Germany, circa 1880, included are three painted wooden furnishings, including fretwork carved bench, three drawer chest with bone knobs, and a wooden rush-bottom chair with embossed floral decorations. $300/500

220.

221. German Bisque Doll with Blonde Curly Hair with Doll's Doll

11" (28 cm.) Bisque shoulder head, blonde very curly hair, painted facial features, muslin body, bisque lower limbs, painted black laced boots, white stockings. Condition: generally excellent. Marks: 256. Comments: Germany, circa 1885, the doll wears her original costume including unusual fitted fingerless kid gloves, and carries a smaller bisque doll with sculpted hair and hair ribbon, wearing antique dress. $400/600

222. German All-Bisque Boy with Toy Horse

6" (15 cm.) One piece bisque head and torso, painted facial features, blonde mohair wig, peg-jointed bisque arms and legs, painted white stockings and blue heeled shoes, wearing red knit suit and cap. Condition: generally excellent. Marks: 32/4. Comments: Germany, circa 1885, the little blue-booted boy owns a miniature pull-toy wheeled horse by Lineol, Germany, and a leather satchel. $300/400

221.

222.

223.

225. *A Small Danish Brick Home Known As "Margretes RO"*

15"h x 18"w x 12"d. A thick-wall wooden single-room cottage has painted faux-brick exterior with an angled roof with outlined shingles and single chimney. The door, at the narrow side of the house, is paint-grained and paneled, surmounted by a steepled frame and fronted by attached steps. There are two windows at both the front and back with fancy wood-grained framed and stenciled decorations. The name "Margretes RO" is arched above the door on a dark banner with gilt lettering. The back removes for access to the single unfurnished room interior with original blue paper walls with gilt paper edging, lace curtains, and glued-wool carpet. A charming cottage with unusual architectural detail, owner's name, and good original condition. The name Margrete is particularly favored in Denmark, having been the name of several historic Queens of that country. Mid-19th century, Denmark. $2000/2500

223. *Early Miniature Hand-tinted Engraving*

2.5" (6 cm.) A rectangular gilt-paper framed engraving portraying a little girl skipping through the park is vividly hand-tinted. Very good condition, slight water spot. Circa 1849. $200/300

224. *Lot of Miniature Pewter Dollhouse Dishes*

2" (5 cm.) 2" teaport holder. Each is made of pewter or silver soft metal, comprising teapot on stand with alcohol burner beneath, lidded compote, large bowl, coffee pot with elegant shape, pitcher, creamer, plate, oval platter, six cups and saucers. Excellent condition. Germany, circa 1890. $300/400

224.

225 .

225 detail.

226 detail.

226. German Two-Room Dollhouse with Rare Roof Garden

15"h. x 30"w. x 18"d. A wooden frame stage-like setting features a large parlor and a small bedroom, with three decorative columns at the front and an interior wall with opening door. There is a large alcove at the rear of the parlor with a window that hinges open at the center, and its roof forming a garden area with wooden balustrade. There are 2 additional windows at the back, each with elaborately carved valance and nice old silk curtains. The wallpaper is a bit peeling, but old and may be original; there are two different paper lithographed floor patterns. Furnishings include 3 maroon velvet armchairs and 2 day beds, painted cardboard parlor stove, oak game table with chessboard top, heavy metal pedestal, and painted white wood bedroom set comprising dresser with mirror, nightstand with marble top, 2 chairs with woven seats and a towel bar. Accessories include ormolu telephone with bells, gilded soft metal magazine holder with old newspapers, soft metal hanging mirror, two-arm sconce with milk glass globes, silvered bird cage with bird, hanging tapestry, hanging chandelier, two nice lithographed paintings, and an early miniature photograph of old woman in silver frame with crown crest. There is a black-haired china doll included. Germany, circa 1890. $2500/3500

227. Four German Bisque Dollhouse Gentlemen

6" (15 cm.) Each has bisque shoulder head with sculpted brown hair,

painted facial features, three having sculpted moustaches, muslin body, bisque lower limbs, painted shoes or boots. Condition: generally excellent. Comments: Germany, circa 1890. Value Points: the gentlemen each wear factory original costumes (albeit a bit faded). $500/800

228. *Fine Large German Two-Room Dollhouse with Biedermeier Furnishings*

13"h. x 24"w. x 13"d. A wooden framed stage-like setting with unusual brick exterior features a finely furnished dining room, adjoined to a small garden room with opening door between. The setting has three ornamental columns at the front, while there are three large six-pane windows at the rear, each with carved canopy and curtains. The rooms have old wallpaper and paper lithographed floors in wood patterns, and there is a ceiling chandelier in each room. The dining room is furnished in Biedermeier style comprising hutch with mirror, table, 4 chairs with silk upholstery, two-drawer dresser, desk with 2 cupboards and niches, and a clock with faux bone columns. The garden room has painted white furnishings with an unusual tea table, of which the top is a tin lithographed lift-out tray with blue-stenciled designs, and the chairs are stamped "CU" (intertwined in circle mark). Accessories include silver soft metal inkwell, tea service, sewing stand, and three tier stand with marble shelf. There is an unusual carved bone table lamp, painted metal stove with coal bucket decorated with decoupage, 2 bisque statues, 2 lithographed portraits, hanging embroidered tapestry, woven carpet, 2 gilded mirrors, fine early framed engraving labeled "Mrs Carnac", and an early miniature pastel of older man, set in silver brooch frame. A richly furnished arrangement with unusual pieces, also featuring a bisque head gentleman with modeled top hat. Circa 1885. $2500/3500

229. *Silver Filigree Miniature Bird Cage*

20" (51 cm.) A very delicate silver filigree birdcage with silver bells and scalloped edging contains a tiny silver bird. Excellent condition. $200/300

229.

228 details.

230.

231.

232.

230. German All-Bisque Doll with Furnishings and Tea Service

7" (18 cm.) Bisque swivel head on kid-edged bisque torso, blue glass inset eyes, painted facial features, slightly open mouth, teeth, blonde mohair wig, peg-jointed body, painted shoes and socks, antique green silk dress. Condition: hairline at right throat and tiny flakes at neck edge, left thumb chipped off. Comments: Germany, circa 1900, included with the large swivel head doll is a wooden garden set with floral chintz upholstery, and matching table with gilt-decorated porcelain tea service. $400/600

231. Set of 19th Century Tin Garden Furniture with Four All-Bisque Dolls

2.5" (6 cm.) 2 1/2" dolls. Each is all-bisque with painted facial features, mohair wig, peg-jointed body, painted shoes, antique costume, two with swivel head. The dolls are posed on tin garden furniture comprising of pedestal table with matching bench and chair, slatted bench and two additional chair. Dolls excellent, furniture has original finish with some paint rubs. Circa 1890. $300/400

232. Three Miniature Porcelain Tea Sets

1.5" (4 cm.) 1 1/2"h. teapots. Each is porcelain with painted decorations, including two with rich gold leaf decorations (one with wooden tray and one with self tray), and a very fine hand-painted example with gold-edged handles and edging around a rich green border and floral decorations. Excellent condition. Early 20th century. $200/300

233. A Two-Story Wooden Doll House with Painted Window Flowers Known as the "Skottenborg House"

31"h. x 19"w. x 12"d. A two-story wooden house with thick exterior walls features a very steeped roof with high angled windowless dormer on one side; the house is painted an original pale green with brown/red roof and trim, and rests upon a thick wooden base that protrudes at the front for placement of flowers or garden pots. There is a six-pane attic window that peeks into a large attic to which there appears to be no access. Fancy architectural carvings edge the front roof line.The second floor features three windows with tin casings and pane frames; flowers are painted on one window. There is a curved wooden spindled balcony in front of the windows. At the lower floor is a center tin door flanked by 2 tin-framed windows. The front hinges open to two rooms, with high ceiling in first floor room. There are plain wooden floors, and walls have been repapered. The half-scale furnishings include settee, 4 chairs, stool, piano, marble top table, fireplace, 2 drawer chest, hall mirror, and desk; accessories include wall pictures and statuary. There are 2 small china dolls. The house, known in the Lego Foundation Museum inventory as the "Skottenborg House", is shown in Jacobs' *A History of*

233 detail.

Dolls Houses (1965) on page 232 as one of a "street of houses" then in the collection of Estrid Faurholt, whose collection was later acquired by the Lego Foundation Museum. $3500/5500

234. German Bisque Doll with Tin Carriage and Bisque Baby

6.5" (17 cm.) Bisque shoulder head with blonde sculpted short curly hair, painted facial features, muslin body, bisque lower limbs, wearing antique costume. Condition: generally excellent. Comments: Germany, circa 1880, included is an early tin carriage with spoked wheels and original cloth sunshade, containing a small all-bisque doll with sculpted hair and jointed limbs, the legs being an unusual bent baby style, antique gown. $400/600

235. German Bisque Doll by Kuhnlenz

9" (23 cm.) Bisque socket head, painted facial features, brunette hair, five piece paper mache body. Condition: generally excellent. The doll is wearing an early cotton twill workman's khaki uniform, green apron, straw hat, and carries various tools viz. scissors, jackknife. $200/300

236. Wonderful Miniature Wooden Stable in Its Original Trunk

7" (18 cm.) 7"w. x 3"h. x 5"d. A wooden trunk with stencil-design paper lithography cover and wooden slat trim, opens to striped paper lining, and lift-out trunk. Stored inside the trunk is a miniature 4"l. wooden stable with painted detail, two large trees, a large number of fence partitions, two lamp posts, a large tree stand, 13 people each with painted costumes including one man on horseback, flower baskets and little shrubs, and more than 35 different wooden farm animals including cows, horses, lambs, goats, dog, and pigs. Excellent unplayed with condition with original painted finishes wonderfully preserved. Circa 1900. $500/800

234.

235, 236.

237. *Early Commercial Stable with Apartment, Windmill and Animals*

17" (43 cm.) 17"h x 12"w x 10" d. A wooden stable with natural finish features two horse stalls with hay rack and chains, and a a carriage stall; an attached inside wooden ladder leads to the second floor apartment with two open arched floor-to-ceiling window openings with fancy arched steepled frames that center a decoupage family crest, fronted by a full-width wooden balcony. There is a carved design at the top of the roof and a chimney with revolving windmill. The base of the stable extends forward serving as a base to display the paper mache gentleman with original wooden base, his various painting roosters and chickens with brightly painted feathers and wooden bases, and the rooster perched upon a basket of eggs (Lineol, German). Excellent condition, late 19th century. $2000/2500

238. *An Early Miniature Tinplate Carriage with Horse*

9" (23 cm.) 9"l. overall. A wooden carved horse with tan flocked finish, painted eyes, real mane, ears, tiny wheeled base, rich leather harness is attached to a tinplate carriage with driver's seat, cushions at the side with original padded upholstery, foot rails and two spoked wheels. Excellent condition, a rare model in well-preserved original state. Circa 1870. $400/600

239. *German Porcelain Miniature with Wood-Articulated Body*

5" (13 cm.) Porcelain shoulder head with short black painted boyish hair, stippling detail around the face, painted facial features, wooden body with shaped torso, dowel jointing at shoulders, elbows, hips and knees, porcelain lower arms and legs, painted orange shoes. Condition: generally excellent. Comments: Germany, circa 1850, the doll wears his original black velvet suit with shirt and tie. $400/600

240. *Charming German Paper Mache Bonnet Doll in Rare Size*

8" (20 cm.) Paper mache shoulder head with painted short brown hair beneath a sculpted blue tam with red edging and real pom-pom, painted facial features, muslin waist area, one-piece paper mache body from waist downward, painted yellow stockings and black boots on shapely legs. Condition: generally excellent, near reglue of right leg above the knee. Comments: Germany, circa 1860, rare model in unusual size with rare body, wearing original cotton costume. $300/500

241. *Tiny Grodnertal Wooden Doll as Sewing Accessory*

4" (10 cm.) Carved wooden head and torso, painted black hair with Tuck comb decoration, painted facial features, wooden arms with dowel jointing at shoulder and elbows. Condition: very good, original paint albeit scuffed at comb. Comments: Grodnertal, circa 1830, the doll has original wooden spool lower body that is covered by red and black wool felt gown decorated the beads; the sewing accessory doll was used to hold thread beneath the skirt, while the skirt could be used as a pin or needle cushion. $300/400

242. *Large Early German Paper Mache Doll with Glass Eyes*

29" (74 cm.) Solid domed paper mache shoulder head with strong elongated throat, black painted hair close to head with looped wave in front of sculpted ears, black enamel inset eyes, painted facial features, closed mouth, old muslin stitch-jointed body, leather arms. Condition: very good, original finish with some fading of features, some craquelure at back of hair. Comments: Germany, circa 1840, an early model with strong and appealing personality, the doll wears wonderful original costume of wools and cotton, great shoes with thick leather soles. $900/1300

243. *Large Group of German Maple Dollhouse Furnishings*

3.5" (9 cm.) 3.5h. desk, 13 pieces plus accessories. Of fine polished maple with natural finish, the group comprises rare Davenport style desk with side drawers, marble top three drawer desk, marble top desk with fancily carved legs and two cubicles, turtle-shaped marble top table, glass front dining cupboard with display shelf, dining table, arm chair with rush seat, balloon back chair with velvet seat, two Gothic style chairs with woven seats and backs, sewing table with fitting interior drawer, velvet-seated piano stool, and a folding tea table that bears the label of Theodore Thorngreen on the underside. Also included is a miniature pewter tea service, and a fine thick needlework fringed carpet. Excellent condition. Germany, circa 1885. $800/1200

244. *Group of Miniature Dollhouse Candle Holders*

3.5" (9 cm.) 3.5" largest. 13 singles, and 5 pairs. Of various styles, the group comprises one pair paint decorated wooden with floral designed bases, and 5 single wooden candle holders; one pair of heavy cast bronze candlestick holders in very ornate style, 3 pair of pewter candle holders, 7 pair of single pewter or metal candle holders in various simple or ornate style, and a single brass candle stick with spiral form. Excellent condition. Circa 1885. $300/500

245. *Important Group of German Dollhouse Furnishings Known as Biedermeier*

4.5" (11 cm.) 4.5"h. piano, 10 pieces. Each of wood with paper lithographed faux-mahogany and gilt stenciled finish, comprising upright piano with hinged

keyboard cover, recamier with original green silk upholstery, sewing table with fitted drawer holding a tiny scissors, desk with cubicles and niches, game table, oval pedestal table, three large arm chairs with very fancy backs and original (frail) magenta silk upholstery, and a small side chair with original green silk upholstery. Very good to excellent condition. Germany, circa 1880. $900/1300

246. *Five Dollhouse Pictures in Original Frames*

4.5" (11 cm.) 4.5" x 4" largest. The group comprises lithograph of village church in elaborate faux-wood gesso frame; an original watercolor of children with flowers in gilded metal frame; an early engraving of 1840 era woman at the dress shop while her husband looks on at the fitting, a pressed cardboard fancy frame with varnished lithographed applied to the front; and a superb early woodcut style scene of family in a Danish boat with hint of mountains in the background in gilded metal frame. Excellent condition. $400/600

247. Group of German Wooden Biedermeier Furniture

5.5" (14 cm.) 5.5"h. chest. 9 pieces. The group of early classic style furnishings includes a cherry wood display cabinet with mirrored back and ebony columns, drop-front desk with faux-ivory columns and six-drawer maple front drawers at the interior, 4-drawer with faux-wood graining and ebony edging, small table with faux-wood grain and shapely maple legs, four chairs including two with rush seats, round tray, and a gentleman's shaving mirror. Excellent condition, one chair seat damaged, shaving mirror faux-drawer-front missing. Germany, circa 1875. $700/1000

248. Group, Early Wooden Dollhouse Furnishings with Denmark Toy Store Labels

7" (18 cm.) 7"h. cupboard, 10 pieces. Each is wood with steam-pressed carved detail at the doors or chair backs, including large cupboard with silverware drawers and narrow side doors, smaller kitchen cupboard with two-shelved upper glass-door top, red-stained camel back sofa with green velvet upholstery and matching chair with fringe, similar chair with red upholstery and brown stain, brown-stained camel back sofa with mauve velvet upholstery, and pair of fancy arm chairs with velvet upholstery. Also included is silver metal three-arm candelabra and wooden potted flower. The hutches and red chairs are stamped H.P. Jensen Ostergade 17; and the arm chairs are marked with the Theodor Thorngreen toy store label. Excellent condition. Circa 1890. $600/1000

249. *Group of German Wooden Dollhouse Furnishings Known as Biedermeier*

4.5" (11 cm.) 4.5"h. piano. 10 pieces. Each is of soft wood with stained and stenciled lithographed cover to simulate mahogany finish with stencilled gilt designs; comprising upright piano with built-in clock (missing keyboard cover), two hall mirrors with marble tops (one with cracked mirror), sewing table with attached wooden lidded jar, desk with cubicles and niches, small table, recamier with green silk upholstery, sofa with green silk upholstery, two balloon-back carved crest side chairs. Germany, circa 1880, good to very good condition. $600/900

250. *German Wooden Dollhouse Bedroom with Original Bed Covers*

7" (18 cm.) 7" armoire. 5 pieces. The oak or chestnut finished bedroom set is decorated with paint-stenciled garlands and flowers, and has very ornate silver hardware, including armoire with narrow centered full mirror, three drawer chest with attached mirror and fancy shelving, small table, and two beds with lace-edged sateen bed covers and pillows. Excellent condition. Circa 1910. $300/500

251. German Bank as Roll-top Desk, Along with Bisque Top-Hat Gentleman

9" (23 cm.) doll. The 7"h. wooden roll-top desk of strong proportions is decorated with wood-grained lithographed paper to suggest rich carving and various drawers and doors that are illusions, although the roll-top is actual. A coin slot at the front accesses to a large compartment at the back with locking key. Included is a bisque shoulder head doll portraying a gentleman with brown sculpted hair beneath a tall black hat, painted facial features, muslin body, bisque lower limbs, antique costume. Excellent condition of doll and desk. Germany, circa 1890. $800/1200

252. Group, Miniature Games and Game Table

4" (10 cm.) 4"h. table. Included is a brown oak miniature game table with very fancy carved pedestal base, heavy board reversible sliding top with chess board on one side and another game on the reverse, having interior compartments containing various game pieces, finely carved chess pieces and miniature dominoes; along with a small wooden game box with chess top and some interior-stored game pieces, desk of miniature paper cards, and an early stenciled tinplate money box with toy silver and gold coins. Excellent condition. Circa 1890. $300/500

253. German Bisque Dollhouse Man with Office Miniature Accessories

5.5" (14 cm.) Bisque shoulder head portraying adult man with brown painted hair and facial features, muslin body, bisque lower limbs, painted brown shoes, wearing original brown flannel business suit. Oak desk along with the following office-themed accessories: soft metal typewriter with working roller, soft metal cigar cutter, soft metal inkwell and blotter, wireless, brass compass and Art Nouveau style easel frame, stationery and dictionary, green metal inkwell with faux marble finish, potted plant, silver-plated opera glasses, a tiny book-shaped box embossed "Somebody's luggage" that hinges open to reveal photograph album, and a silver-framed miniature sepia photograph, perhaps of the gentleman's mother. Good to excellent condition. Circa 1910. $500/800

254. Early and Very Rare Miniature Dollhouse Priest with Liturgical Accessories

6" (15 cm.) A waxed dowel head with painted features and grey real hair wig and beard has original wooden body with dowel jointing at shoulder and hips, painted stockings and brown boots. Condition: generally excellent. Comments: early 19th century, the priest is wearing an elaborate silk costume with richly embroidered details; also includes a matching silk table cover and various other liturgical elements. $400/600

255. *German All-Bisque Doll in Danish Costume with Furnishings*

5" (13 cm.) One piece bisque head and torso, sculpted curly brown hair, painted facial features, jointed limbs, wearing original Danish costume with woolen costume, red wool petticoat, warm scarf, along with wooden dining room dollhouse furnishings comprising table with one drop leaf, and silverware drawers at either end and three matching chairs with pressed-carving and faux-leather seats. Condition: generally excellent, one table leaf may be missing. Circa 1920, the chairs are marked "H.P. Jensen". $300/400

256. *German Bisque Dollhouse Lady with Sewing Accessories*

6" (15 cm.) Bisque shoulder head lady with blonde sculpted hair, painted facial features, muslin body, bisque lower limbs, wearing factory original cotton house dress and pantalets, marked 418 10/0. Along with an early handmade cotton dress, a gilded soft metal sewing basket with thimble, two scissors, wooden darning egg, tiny buttons, brass embossed photo album with four tiny sepia photographs of military men, leather purse, leatherette needle case, two miniature silhouettes, gesso plaque of woman and cherub, candle holder, teething ring, box of carved faux ivory chains, miniature tatting frame and a velvet cushion. Late 19th to early 20th century. Excellent condition. $300/400

257. *German Bisque Doll as Nun with Two Smaller Nun Dolls*

8" (20 cm.) Bisque shoulder head doll with painted facial features, muslin body and bisque limbs, is wearing an elaborately layered original nun's habit with accessories. Included are two additional smaller bisque dolls wearing nun's habits. Germany, circa 1890. $400/600

258. *Miniature Religious-themed Dollhouse Accessories*

5" (13 cm.) 5" largest cross. Included is white porcelain trinket box as altar with separate lid (one urn has tiny chip), and three wooden or metal crucifix. $200/300

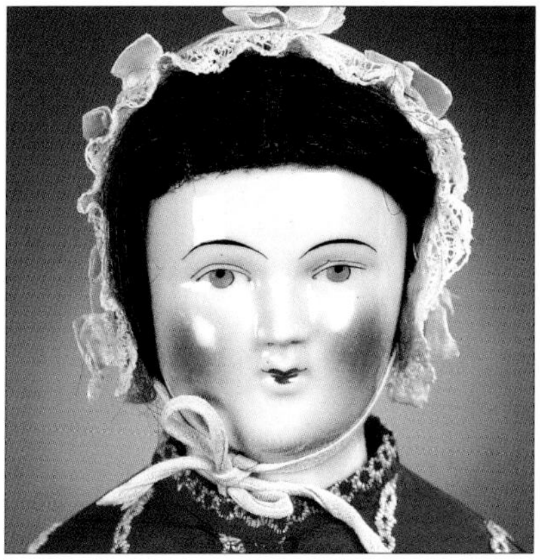

259. *German Porcelain Doll with Wig and Antique Costume*

21" (53 cm.) Solid domed porcelain shoulder head, black painted pate under hand-tied brunette human hair wig, painted facial features, closed mouth, muslin stitch-jointed body, porcelain arms. Condition: generally excellent, porcelain arms mis-matched. Marks: 11 (inside shoulder plate). Comments: Germany, circa 1875, the rosy-cheeked doll wears antique costume and cap. $300/400

260.

261.

262.

263.

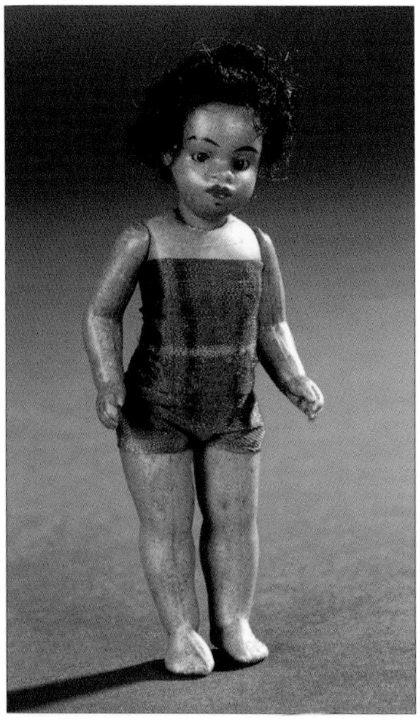

264.

265.

260. *German Black-Complexioned All-Bisque Doll in Blue Knit*

5" (13 cm.) Black bisque swivel head on black bisque torso, black glass eyes, closed mouth, black fleeced hair, loop-jointed arms and legs, bare feet, nicely costumed. Condition: lower torso reglued, both ankles reglued. Marks: 61.12. Comments: Kuhnlenz, circa 1890, great character expression. $300/400

261. *Two German Black-Complexioned All-Bisque Dolls*

3.5" (9 cm.) One with painted eyes and solid head and torso, one with glass eyes and swivel head, each with painted facial features, jointed arms and legs, fleeced hair, antique red woolen costumes. Condition: swivel head with tiny flakes at torso neck. Comments: Germany, circa 1900. $300/400

262. *German Black-Complexioned All-Bisque Googly*

3.5" (9 cm.) Ebony-black complexioned all-bisque doll has swivel head, glass inset round googly eyes, painted facial features, closed mouth, fleeced hair, loop-jointed bisque arms and legs, painted blue socks and black shoes, red cotton dress. Condition: generally excellent, tiniest flakes at toe tip and leg string holes. Marks: 293 8. Comments: German, circa 1915. $400/500

263. *German All-Bisque Portrait of Asian Man with Hat*

2.5" (6 cm.) One-piece amber tinted bisque head and torso with sculpted yellow hat, painted facial features, pin-jointed bisque arms and legs, painted black shoes, orange silk kimono. Condition: generally excellent. Marks: Germany. Comments: circa 1900. $300/400

264. *German All-Bisque with Café-au-Lait Complexion*

4.5" (11 cm.) Light brown ("café-au-lait") complexioned all-bisque with swivel head, bisque torso, black glass eyes, closed mouth, painted facial features, black fleecy hair, loop-jointed bisque arms and legs, bare feet. Condition: generally excellent, tiniest flake at torso front neck and at top of right thigh. Marks: 61-10. Comments: Kuhnlenz, circa 1890. $300/400

265. *German All-Bisque with Amber Brown Complexion*

4.5" (11 cm.) Golden amber complexioned all-bisque with swivel head, bisque torso, black glass eyes, closed mouth, painted facial features, black fleecy hair, loop-jointed bisque arms and legs, bare feet. Condition: generally excellent. Marks: 61-10. Comments: Kuhnlenz, circa 1890, the doll wears fragments of its original costume including bracelets and turban. $300/400

266. *German All-Bisque Boy with Lamb*

5" (13 cm.) Bisque swivel head on kid-edged bisque torso, brown glass inset eyes, closed mouth, painted features, loop-jointed bisque arms and legs, painted shoes and stockings. Condition: restoration at back lower torso, reglue at left leg. Marks: 31 12. Comments: Kestner, circa 1890, the doll wears its original red and cream knit suit, and carries little fleecy paper mache lamb. $400/500

267. *German All-Bisque Boy and Girl in Original Costumes*

5.5" (14 cm.) Each has bisque swivel head on kid-edged bisque torso, brown glass inset eyes, slightly parted lips, teeth, painted facial features, blonde mohair wig, peg-jointed bisque arms and legs, painted white socks and brown one-strap shoes. Condition: girl has flakes at upper thigh, boy has spiderweb hairline at back of head. Marks: 31.14. Comments: Kuhnlenz, circa 1890, the beautiful pair wear their factory original knit costumes. $700/900

268. *German All-Bisque Boy in Original Sailor Costume*

5" (13 cm.) One-piece bisque head and torso, brown glass inset eyes, closed mouth, painted features, brunette bobbed wig, jointed bisque arms and legs, painted stockings and black two-strap shoes. Condition: generally excellent, tiny flakes underside of left finger tips. Marks: 61-5. Comments: circa 1890, the little boy wears his factory original sailor suit and cap. $300/400

269. *French All-Bisque Girl with Miniature Bisque Statue*

4" (10 cm.) Bisque swivel head on kid-edged bisque torso, blue glass enamel inset eyes, closed mouth, painted facial features, peg-jointed bisque arms and legs, painted white stockings, blue two-strap shoes, original costume. Condition: generally excellent, small chip at front torso and left shoulder. Comments: French, circa 1890, included is a white statue depicting a young boy with his beloved dog. $300/400

270.

270. *A Fine Early Danish Dollhouse Room, "Charlotte's Lyst", with Musical Piano*

16" (41 cm.) A thick wooden-framed room with angled sides and a roof has two large side windows with painted panes and a built-in faux-marble fireplace with wall-paper covered chimney and fancy mantel. The walls have old embossed fleur-de-lis wallpaper, and a gilded fancy four-arm chandelier hangs from the ceiling that is painted with a fancy stenciled design. There are carved window valances and lace curtains. Furnishings include 2 early painted carved wood-painted chairs with maple legs and decoupage, early painted tin table with 2 side chairs and a rocker with silk pillow, other chairs, painted metal stove, Biedermeier style furnishings including secretaire with drop front and fancy interior and an upright piano that plays music when manivelle handle at the back is turned (the piano is stamped F. Thomsens, leger af Harmonikaer, Stue-Orgeier...K Jobenhavn".) Accessories include wedding photograph in silver frame, carved bone inkwell set, mini book "Poems Chiefly in the Scottish Dialect", hanging gilded and wooden mirrors, die-cast figural of man on a donkey, metal figural clock of man walking in the forest that fits into its original porcelain base, 3 lithographed framed scenes, tiny sewing box of punched paper, and wood and bone foot stool with velvet cushion, and a cross-stitch rug. A black-haired china doll lives in the room. An accompanying label reads "Charlotte's Lyst". Circa 1880. $3000/4000

271. *German Wooden Dollhouse Room with Large Oak Dining Furniture*

14" (36 cm.) A wooden stage-like room setting features painted red walls, wood floor, two large curtained windows at the back, a full-length mirror and fireplace that appears to be attached but is not, and a large needlework patterned carpet. The room is furnished with

271.

a large-size oak dining set comprising round pedestal table with pressed carving on the surface, 3 matching table chairs, 2 rockers and a sofa with unusual green leather upholstery having pressed designs, 2 matching beds with bed covers, wood dish cabinet with doors and drawer, and a wooden side table. Accessories include soft metal magazine holder and flower stand containing 3 potted flowers, 4 very nice lithographed paintings, metal plates and urns, table clock, and two miniature dogs. There are two black hair china dolls and 2 bisque dolls with blonde sculpted hair included. Germany, circa 1900. $1500/2000

272. A Well-Furnished German Two Room Wooden Dollhouse

11" (28 cm.) A wooden framed two-room stage-like setting with connecting door, has three large curtained windows at the back, especially nice paper wallpaper and lithographed faux-wood floors. The parlor is furnished with a maple table with marble top, maple desk, and silk upholstered loveseat and 2 arm chairs, each with unusual stenciled design to suggest carving. The dining room features a maple wood dining table, 4 wood chairs in the Gothic style with woven seats, and fancy cupboard. Accessories include maple hanging pendulum clock, tin stove and coal bucket, gilded soft metal oil lamp with ruby shade, soft metal telephone, clock, painted wood pedestal, framed lithograph of children riding a pony, silk screen of a winter scene, soft metal serving table, gilded flower vases, soft metal tea service and cruet set, milk glass dishes, sewing basket, and other wall decorations. There are two early dollhouse dolls included. A label at the side of the house reads "Dukkestue 2v. 1900". Circa 1900. $1200/1800

272 detail.

273. Nine Antique Dollhouse Ceiling Lamps

2" (5 cm.) 2" silver chandelier excluding chain. The group includes six-arm silver soft metal candelabra, gilded soft metal 4-arm chandelier with milk glass shades, gilded 3-arm soft metal chandelier with milk glass petal shaped shades (shades damaged, one missing), silver soft metal chandelier with three green teardrop shades, green glass hanging globe, red silk hanging fixture with beaded fringe, small 3-arm silver candelabra, gilded metal hanging oil lamp with original glass chimney, and a suspended opalescent glass globe with painted decorations and brass rim. Included is a silver wall sconce with green glass globe. Very good to excellent condition. Circa 1890/1920. $500/800

273.

274 detail.

274. A Faux-Brick Three Story English Doll House Known as the "Emscott House"

33"h x 19"w x 12"d. A narrow-shaped tall wooden house with painted faux-brick finish features 7 front windows of three varying sizes, each with well-detailed wooden panes and wide sills designed for holding window pots. The solid panel front door is surmounted by a non-opening transom window. The sides and back of the house are solid. The front hinges open to reveal three large rooms, one on each floor, connected by stairs in the narrow hallway with opening doors into the rooms. The paper in the house is old, but may not be original; the floors are plain wood. There is a hat rack and umbrella stand in the front hall, and other furnishings include Maerklin fireplace, maple desk, 5 upholstered seating pieces, chest, and a 5-piece maple bedroom set including a marble top washstand. Accessories include 3 ormolu framed pictures, 2 oil lamps, birdcage, 2 "portraits", clock, wash bowl, and a cradle; there are three bisque dollhouse dolls and an all-bisque child. A hand-lettered sign on the glass transom window reads "Emscott, 90, Anerley [sic] Park, S.E." Late 19th century. $2500/3500

275.

275. Pair, German Bisque Dolls with Sculpted Hair by Alt, Beck & Gottschalk

10" (25 cm.) Each has bisque shoulder head with blonde sculpted short curly hair, painted facial features, muslin body, bisque lower limbs with painted black heeled boots and stockings, antique costumes. Condition: generally excellent. Marks: 1064 #3/0 (girl) 1222 #3/0 (boy). Comments: Alt, Beck & Gottschalk, circa 1885. $300/400

276.

276. Two Large German All-Bisque Dolls, Attributed to Hertwig

9" (23 cm.) Each has one-piece head and torso with pale complexion, sculpted short blonde curly hair, pin-jointed bisque arms and legs, painted white stockings and blue rims, black one-strap shoes. Condition: generally excellent, boy missing left thumb tip. Comments: attributed to Hertwig, circa 1890, the large all-bisque boy and girl wear antique knit costumes. $400/600

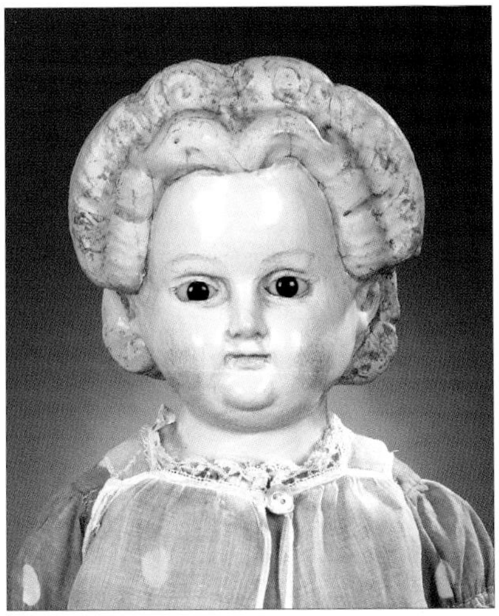

277.

279.

277. Large German Wax over Paper Mache Doll with Original Costume

26" (66 cm.) Wax over paper mache shoulder head with blonde sculpted hair framing the face with wide rolled curls, short page boy curls at the back and painted black hair bow, glass inset eyes, closed mouth, muslin body, wooden lower limbs, painted black flat wooden shoes with gold buttons. Condition: generally excellent. Comments: Germany, circa 1880, the doll has original body, wears original rose cotton gown, pinafore, and undergarments. $400/500

278.

278. German Wax over Paper Mache Lady with Sculpted Bonnet

14" (36 cm.) Wax over paper mache shoulder head of adult woman with sculpted green bonnet over fleecy mohair curls, black enamel eyes, painted facial features, muslin body, wooden lower limbs. Condition: very good, some typical wax fading. Comments: Germany, circa 1875, the doll wears her original white dotted Swiss gown trimmed with silver beads, a pearl cluster, silk flower and feathers in hat, and fancy sash, undergarments. $300/400

279. 19th Century Wooden Toy Feed Mill and Horse

24" (61 cm.) A wooden toy feed mill with painted brick facade has four floors, each with cut-out windows, circular windows on the top floor, a hinged fold-down wooden fenced yard at the front. There are two hinged doors at the front labeled "No.3" and "No 4", and an illegible sign over the front entrance, a bag of feed suspends from the faux-pulley, and there are other bags of feed, and a fleece-covered glass-eyed wooden toy horse on a wooden wheeled base with elaborate saddle and harness. Very good condition. Circa 1880. $700/900

280. *Set of Miniature Enamel-Lined Kitchenware*

2.5" (6 cm.) 2.5" l. muffin dish, 10 pieces. Of heavy cast pottery with black finish, each piece has white porcelain enamel interior, comprising six-cup muffin dish, 2 different molds, one-handled jug (hairline), and six other various pieces. Excellent condition except jug. Circa 1890, a rare set. $200/300

281. *Group of Antique Miniature Wooden Kitchenware*

6" (15 cm.) 6" broom. The group comprises a yellow painted broom, wire-handled bucket, double handled tub, round cutting board with handle, slaw cutter, two plates, and a three-hook rack with Danish porcelain labels for various utensils. Circa 1900. $300/500

282. *Group of Dollhouse Heating Stoves and Coal Buckets*

5" (13 cm.) 5" largest stove. Two stoves of pressed tin with embossed brick or figural design, gold plated doors and crest, and two stoves of painted soft metal are included, along with five different tin coal buckets with hinged lids, gilded handles, one with decoupage of kitten, another with floral decoupage. Circa 1890. $400/600

283. *Two Dollhouse Accessories*

4.5" (11 cm.) 4.5" walnut wall telephone with turning crank, silvered bells, mouthpiece and ear piece, along with tinplate oil lamp with gilt stencil decoration and brass plate at the hanging hook back. Excellent condition. Circa 1890. $300/400

284 details.

284. German Wooden Toy Kitchen with Furnishings

13" (33 cm.) 13"h. x 19"w. x 12"d. A wooden framed room with fancy columns at the sides and two back windows is furnished with full-length wooden counter and sink, built-in wooden plate racks and high shelf, tin stove, wooden table and chair, and has many accessories: 8 porcelain German labeled canisters including salt box, 6 porcelain blue rimmed plates, tinplate oil lamp, pewter bed warmer, 8 blue enamel pots including spoon rack and 2 spoons, and numerous other pots and dishes. Circa 1900. $600/900

285. German Bisque Child Doll by Kling

20" (51 cm.) Bisque shoulder head turned downward, blue glass eyes, closed mouth with pouty expression, painted facial features, brunette mohair wig, kid pin-jointed body, bisque lower arms, wearing antique pink cotton dress, undergarments, shoes, stockings, bonnet. Condition: generally excellent. Comments: Kling, circa 1890. $400/600

286. German Bisque Doll, 167, by Kling

15" (38 cm.) Bisque shoulder head turned slightly to the right, large brown glass eyes, closed mouth with pouty expression, painted features, blonde mohair wig, kid gusset-jointed body, bisque lower arms, wearing antique dotted Swiss dress, undergarments, leather shoes, bonnet. Condition: generally excellent. Marks: 167-4. Comments: Kling, circa 1890, an especially pretty brown-eyed child. $300/500

Apotheke

288.

287. *Collection, German Soft Metal Dollhouse Furnishings*

3" (8 cm.) 3" sewing machine, 18 pieces. Each is of soft metal with silver or gold painted finish and other decorations, including bronzed magazine rack with painted butterfly design on one side and lyre on the other, sewing machine with working treadle, plant stand with exotic green metal plant, fireplace with spigot for heated water, birdcage, mirror with cherubs in fancy frame, floor-standing sewing basket with hinged lid, hanging cabinet, tiny piano, mirror with upper shelf, "apotheke" chest with name embossed on door, pedestal side table with walnut top, fancy flower pot holder, wall clock with pendulum, umbrella stand, inkwell, tiny bed, and Art Nouveau style mirror with figural of woman holding the round beveled mirror. Circa 1900. $700/1000

288. *A Fine German Two Room Furnished Dollhouse with Wide Flower Sills*

12" (30 cm.) 12"h. x 28"w. x 13"d. A wooden framed two-room miniature arrangment has three paned windows at the back with very wide interior sills for holding flower pots, fancy columns at the front, curtains, fancy flowered or patterned wallpaper, paper lithographed faux-wood parquet floors. Furnishings include maple desk with cubicles and niches, wooden sofa and three chairs with pressed carvings and mauve velvet upholstery, maple sewing table with fitted interior filled with sewing notions, ormolu table with patterned chess top, ormolu flat table, soft metal table with marble top, parlor stove, bed, armoire, marble top maple table, silk covered chair. Accessories include soft metal birdcage, 2 clocks, dishes and lamp with fabric shade, ormolu inkwell, blotter and unusual framed desk pad, two brass framed oval paintings, and a brass easel back framed antique photograph of young girl, perhaps the original owner of the house. There are 5 potted plants and a woven cradle, and 2 dolls inhabit the setting. Germany, circa 1900. $1200/1800

288 detail.

289. *Collection of Six Miniature Oil Lamps*

6" (15 cm.) 6" bronzed lamp with milk glass chimney. Included are five various embossed metal oil lamps (four with fancy double handles, two with glass chimneys), and a silver plated unusual oil lamp with three pipes and carrying handle. Also included is unusual early electric lamp with wooden bowl and original light bulb (not known if working). Circa 1910. $400/500

289.

290.

291.

290. *Lot of Various Wooden Dollhouse Furnishings*

5" (13 cm.) 5"h. screen, 14 pieces. Including Hepplewhite style cherry buffet in fine cabinetry, maple country side table, walnut desk with unusual marquetry designs on lid, squirrel cage of unusual design, inlay maple cupboard, music stand, walnut wall mirror with inlay design, oval cherry dining table with elegantly tapered legs, wall mirror with inlay design, four various side chairs, folding screen with beaded design, and a very fine pedestal end table with beautifully inlaid surface. Age unknown of the various pieces. $300/600

291. *Collection of Soft Metal Dishes and Tableware*

2.5" (6 cm.) 2.5" tea wagon, 14 pieces plus accessories. Each of soft metal with gilded or silver finish comprising tea cart with working wheels, pedestal spoon holder with handle and spoons, sewing basket with silk lining, compote bowl on pedestal, compote bowl on tripod, shaving mirror with hinged mirror, cruet holder with amber glass bottles, cruet holder with salt and two bottles, tray with fabric floral pattern and two napkin rings, single candle holder with finger hole, dust pan, tiny mirror, fruit basket with knife holders, another fruit holder. Very good to excellent condition. Circa 1900. $300/400

292. *German Wooden Dollhouse Armoires and Bisque Doll*

6" (15 cm.) 6"doll. Bisque shoulder head with blonde sculpted hair, painted facial features, muslin body, bisque lower limbs, antique dress, marked "131 7/0", along with 3 wooden armoires of different styles and woods, the lime green model having original painted cardboard inserts, the golden oak with gilded metal appliques, stained glass windows and interior coat hooks. Excellent condition. Circa 1890. $200/400

292.

293. *German Bentwood Garden Furniture, Two Dolls and Accessories*

5" (13 cm.) 5" dolls. The ebony-finished bent wood furnishings include pedestal table with floral decoupage, settee and four matching chairs with mauve velvet upholstery, an earthenware and a porcelain bunny, two black haired china dolls with antique costumes and bodies. Excellent condition. Circa 1910. $200/400

294. *Group of Dollhouse Plants and Plant Holders*

4" (10 cm.) 4" 3-tiered stand. Included is a three-tiered tin stand with original paint, round tin pedestal table with paint-grained finish, and a cardboard table with wooden base and pressed cardboard fancy edging; along with a large wooden bucket with faux-tree, and 15 other wooden pots, some paint decorated with faux-flowers. Circa 1900. $300/500

293.

294.

295. *Large and Well-Furnished Turn-of-the-Century German Kitchen with Pantry*

16" (41 cm.) 21"w. x 16"h. x 16"d. A large wooden framed kitchen with large six pane curtained window is painted bright white, featuring a closed door pantry with interior shelves, built-in counter with sink, large cupboard with latched glass doors, and blue and white diamond-patterned checkered floor. There is a cast iron stove laden with tin pots and pans, tin coal bucket, white wooden table and chair. Accessories include large blue wooden hanging and plate rack, spoon rack, a number of blue tin lithographed cooking utensils including unusual fish mold, tin oil lamp, wooden coffee grinder with brass drawer, tin delivery wagon, unusual bread or sausage cutter, well-made carving knife, numerous dishes, bottles and porcelain canister set. A German bisque dollhouse lady with sculpted blonde hair and antique costume stands at the table. Germany, circa 1910. $1100/1600

295 detail.

295.1. *German Porcelain Lady with Fancy Black Hair*

12" (30 cm.) Porcelain shoulder head portraying an adult lady with elongated throat and slender face, sculpted black hair waved away from face in wide curls at the side, cluster of curls at the back of head, painted facial features, muslin stitch-jointed body, porcelain lower arms, antique cotton print gown, apron, undergarments, stockings, shoes. Condition: generally excellent, some finger tip flakes. Comments: Germany, circa 1875. $300/400

296. *German Porcelain Lady with Modeled Snood*

14" (36 cm.) Porcelain shoulder head portraying an adult lady with black sculpted hair arranged with black ribbons at side of head and sculpted black snood, elongated throat, painted facial features with somber expression, early kid leather body with shapely waist and limbs, antique costume. Condition: generally excellent, some body reinforcement. Comments: Germany, circa 1885. $300/400

295.1.

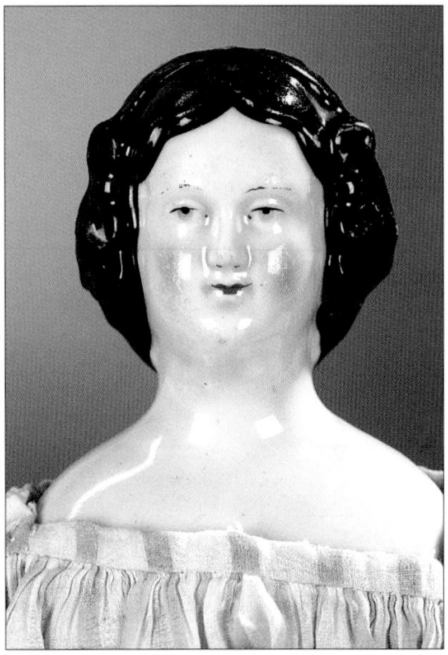

296.

297.

297. *German Grocery Stove with Laden Shelves*

11" (28 cm.) 19"w. x 12" s. x 11"h. A wooden framed grocery store with painted white interior and shelving has blue stenciled design, painted floor, built-in shelving and cupboards, including an unusual cabinet with hinged slanted glass lid, 16 pull-out drawers, tin canisters with stenciled labels, and numerous other miniature goods and accessories including a tin scale with brass plates, tin can labeled "petroleum" and bags, brooms and such. Included is a black haired china head dollhouse man, bisque dollhouse man with moustache as grocer, and two other dolls. Germany, circa 1900. $800/1300

297.1.

297.1. *Two All-Original German Bisque Dollhouse Dolls*

6" (15 cm.) Each has bisque shoulder head with sculpted hair and painted facial features, muslin body, bisque lower limbs and painted shoes. Condition: generally excellent. Comments: Germany, circa 1900, the pair includes a baker or shopkeeper gentleman with modeled moustache, and lady going to market, each wearing factory-original costume. $300/400

298. *Petite German Bisque Lady with Antique Costume*

9" (23 cm.) Pale bisque shoulder head with short blonde sculpted hair, painted facial features, blue eyes, rosy cheeks, closed mouth, muslin body, bisque lower limbs, painted boots, the doll is wearing an early patterned cotton gown and undergarments. Condition: generally excellent. Comments: Germany, circa 1885. $300/400

298.

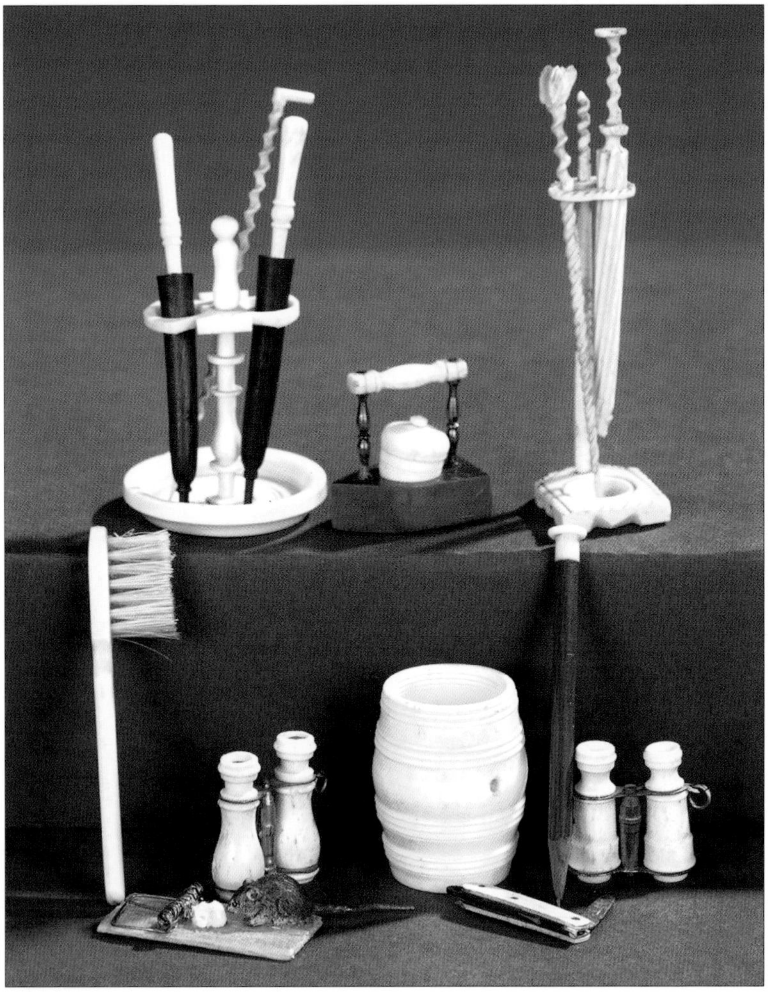

299. Large Collection of Miniature Color Glassware

3" (8 cm.) 3" epergne, 45 pieces. Highlighted by a superb epergne in three delicate colors and an early goblet with hand-painted flowers, the group features miniature vases, pitchers, goblets, lamp, bowls, decorative accessories, and other pieces in a myriad of beautiful colors. Excellent condition. Late 19th century. $400/500

300. Group, French Carved Bone or Ivory Miniature Dollhouse Accessories

1" (3 cm.) 1" flat iron, 8 objects. Each is carved of bone or ivory, including barrel, two umbrella stands with umbrellas (one with spiral walking stick), two pairs of opera glasses (one with French Stanhope images, one with Stanhope images of Copenhagen scenes), toothbrush, iron with cherry form and brass and ivory handle, jar with attached lid, pocket knife, and a tiny wooden mousetrap with mouse and cheese. Excellent condition, circa 1890, except date uncertain on mouse trap. $400/600

301. *German Painted Tin Water Fountain*

4" (10 cm.) Of tin with painted faux-marlbe finish, the wall-hanging fountain features a water tank at the top with hinged lid for actual use and working gilded spigot above a large bowl. Excellent condition. Possibly Maerklin. Circa 1890. $300/400

302. *Group, German Gilded Ormolu Dollhouse Accessories*

7" (18 cm.) 7"h. mirror, 13 objects. Included are large gilt-framed salon mirror with carved crest, small four-legged table or stool with impressed floral design on top, stand with four hooks, umbrella stand, candlestick with Poseidon-shaped handle, desk blotter, two paper holders, candlestick with loop handle, miniature hanging clock with porcelain face, scroll-columned single candlestick, blue glass bud vase with fancy holder, crumb broom frame, hook, napkin ring, and fancy serving spoon with shell-shaped bowl. Excellent condition. Germany, circa 1890. $600/900

303. *Collection of Miniature Porcelain Tableware*

2" (5 cm.) 2" clock. Featuring two porcelain tea services with trays, and 15 additional pieces comprising pitcher, faux-clock with painted face, porcelain inkwell, richly painted fruit bowl, bisque figure (little chip on skirt), Chinese bowl, and others. Excellent condition except as note. Late 19th century. $300/400

304. Unusual Wooden Five-Room House with Brick Facade

304 detail.

12" (30 cm.) 30"l. x 18"d. x 12"h. A one-story house with an unusually large five rooms on the single door has removable roof and back wall for play access. The exterior is painted faux-red-brick on all four sides with a green opening arched front door above wooden steps. There are 12 curtained windows, and interior doors opening into each room. The low-sloped roof has painted green shingles with a fancily carved roof edging with stenciled border, and two carved chimneys. There are five interior rooms, each with old (but possibly not original) wall papers (the kitchen with Dutch tile paper) and painted floors. Furnishings include a fine maple parlor set with three Gothic style chairs and a massive sofa, each with luxurious maroon velvet upholstery and fringe, each signed H.P. Jensen; along with marble-top hall mirror, marble top chest, maple table, hanging corner cupboard with fretwork carving, tall statue pedestal, maple tavern table, three Gothic maple chairs with pressed woven seats, maple buffet with pressed carving (signed, illegible), painted white single bed, night table. Accessories include bisque white bust, soft metal birdcage, and fernery, needlework carpet, alarm clock, ormolu framed lithograph, tiny woven cradle with doll, and various china, glassware, and tableware. Germany, circa 1890. $2500/3500

304 detail.

305. *German All-Bisque Doll with Chairs and Pets*

4" (10 cm.) doll. Bisque swivel head on kid-edged bisue torso, brown glass inset eyes, closed mouth, blonde mohair wig, peg-jointed bisque arms and legs, painted shoes and stockings, wearing factory original knit dress and muslin undergarments. Condition: generally excellent. Comments: Germany, circa 1900, included are three ebony bentwood chairs and an all-bisque Spaniel puppy and cat. $400/500

306. *German All-Bisque Boy with Porcelain Dog and Cart*

4" (10 cm.) doll. All-bisque doll with swivel head, glass eyes, closed mouth, painted features, blonde mohair wig, peg-jointed limbs, wearing antique purple velvet page boy costume with leather boots. Condition: generally excellent. Marks: 10 31. Comments: circa 1900, the wonderfully costumed little boy owns a porcelain bulldog with white collar and harness that is pulling a small open-seat metal cart with bronzed finish. $500/700

307. *German All-Bisque Doll with Tinplate Horse and Carriage Toy*

4" (10 cm.) doll. All-bisque doll with swivel head, glass eyes, closed mouth, painted features, blonde mohair wig, peg-jointed limbs, wearing factory original blue velvet suit and cap, painted shoes and socks. Condition: generally excellent. Marks: 10 31. Comments: Germany, circa 1890, included is a tinplate horse and buggy with hand-painted details, containing a tiny 2" French all-bisque doll with original factory knit costume. $400/500

308. *German All-Bisque Doll with Toy Pony*

4" (10 cm.) doll. All-bisque doll with swivel head, glass eyes, closed mouth, painted features, blonde mohair wig, peg-jointed limbs, wearing black velvet suit and cap, painted shoes and socks. Condition: generally excellent. Marks: 10 31. Comments: Germany, circa 1890, included is a carved wooden toy horse (one glass eye missing) with mane and harness. $400/500

309. *Pair, German All-Bisque Dolls*

4" (10 cm.) Two all-bisque dolls have swivel head, glass eyes, closed mouth, painted facial features, blonde mohair wig, peg-jointed bisque limbs, painted shoes and socks, antique costumes. Condition: generally excellent, one with chip at back upper torso, flakes at stringing holes. Marks: 31 11. Comments: Germany, circa 1900, included is a smaller all-bisque doll with solid neck, glass eyes, antique costume, hidden inside cardboard candy container valise. $500/700

310. *French All-Bisque Doll with Toy Carriage and Tiny Doll*

4" (10 cm.) doll. All-bisque doll with swivel head, painted facial features, blonde mohair wig, peg-jointed bisque limbs, painted shoes and socks, antique lace dress and undergarments. Condition: generally excellent. Marks: 5. Comments: for the French market, circa 1890, included is a tin lithographed doll stroller with spoke wheels, containing a tiny all bisque doll with painted features and original costume. $400/500

311. Early Cardboard Blue Room with Furnishings

11" (28 cm.) A heavy cardboard room with blue paper lined walls and paper-covered floor has two large curtained glass windows at the rear flanking a tall mirror. Furnishings include wooden upright piano, several pieces of Boulle-style wooden furnishings, tin fireplace with fire, hanging tin corner shelf with mirrors, soft metal cuckoo clock, little child's bed, and accessories such as fine quality porcelain lidded tureen, statue of crane, brass wall clock, lithograph of two children with a book, and a statue of a fisherman. Dolls include a black haired china man, and a small but very fine early bisque child with blonde sculpted hair. Fair condition, paper on floor not original. Circa 1865. $800/1300

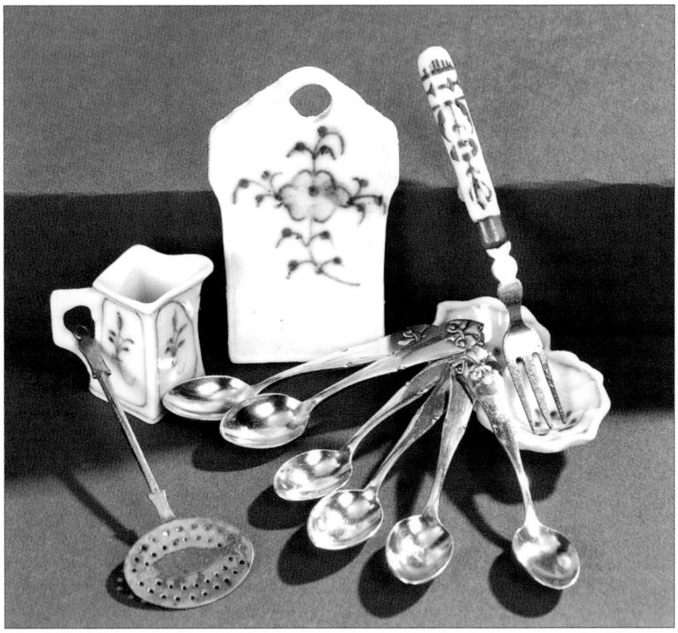

312. Group, Miniature Silver and Porcelain Tableware

3.5" (9 cm.) 3.5" fork. Included are five silver spoons with hallmarks and E.K. initials, serving form with blue and white porcelain handle, a very rare silverplate sieved spoon with an image of a fish for service poached salmon, and 3 piece of white porcelain with cobalt blue stenciled designs, viz. cutting board, pitcher, and handled relish dish. Excellent condition. Late 19th century. $400/500

313. German Porcelain Lady and Little Babies

5.5" (14 cm.) 5.5" doll. An early German black haired porcelain doll has softly looped waves of hair over each ear and joined in a chignon at back of head, painted features, muslin body, porcelain limbs, painted black shoes. Condition: generally excellent. Comments: Germany, circa 1865, included are 5 little all-porcelain bathing dolls known as Frozen Charlotte, an antique wooden doll chair, and a tiny woven baby cradle. $300/400

314. *German Wooden Dollhouse Room with Lithographed Curtains*

10" (25 cm.) A large wooden room has paper lithographed interior walls with rich decoration of late 19th century style room, featuring designs of bordered wall paper, carved valances and draperies and wall pictures and frames, as well as paper lithographed patterned floor. The room is furnished with various pieces including a silk-covered wishbone chair, a rare and beautifully made hall stand with paper lithographed designs of clock and statue and having a lift-top seat, wooden upright piano, bent-wood table, settee, stool and chairs, writing desk with facade of book covers on the bottom shelf. Accessories include 2 mini books ("History of England" and "Kallundborgs Kronthe"), tin tea kettle with heating element, candlesticks, bisque statue of girl on Greek style columned pedestal, ship in a bottle, small carpet, and a bisque dog. Very good condition, some staining on exterior walls. Circa 1890. $1200/1800

315. *A Fine Group of Miniature Silver Tableware*

1.5" (4 cm.) About 1.5" various pots and urns. The group includes 2 tall coffeepots (one with curved legs), two teacots (one with very fancy finial on kid and handle, and spiral twist design of pot), 2 double-handled urns or loving cups, 2 fluted edge trays, large round plate, two small plated with beaded rims, 4 other various pieces, and a rare double-sided tiny pill or poison box with embossed designs. Condition: generally excellent. Comments: late 19th century, a few of the pieces are hallmarked. $600/900

316. *German Black Haired Porcelain Lady and Bisque Baby*

10" (25 cm.) Porcelain shoulder head with black sculpted hair in short curls, painted facial features, muslin body, bisque lower limbs, painted boots, wearing antique costume and undergarments. Condition: generally excellent. Comments: Germany, circa 1890, included is a 5" bisque dollhouse baby with wig, muslin body, bisque lower limbs, wearing a fine silk baby gown with embroidery that encloses a flannel cloth slip designed for use as a pin cushion. $200/300

317 detail.

317. *A Fine Large Dollhouse Kitchen Known as "Dansk Kokken"*

24"w. x 12"h. x 14"d. A Danish-furnished wooden toy kitchen is presented in stage-like form with original painted walls, curtains window, and paper lithographed floor, featuring 3 built-in shelves, 1 large built in plate rack, and a built-in counter top with storage cabinet at the side. The kitchen is furnished by a wood table with swing legs to hold up drop leaves, 2 wooden chair, step-stool, tin stove, and a wooden cabinet with five drawers labeled Gewurz, Pfeffer, Nelken, Zimmt, and Lorbeerblatter. Accessories include innumerable plates, bowls and utensils of wood, china and metal, brass and wood saws and axes, an unusual wood and bone flat iron, set of 6 bottles in carved wood container, a hanging china set of large utensils, and a wooden and bone churn. A German bisque dollhouse doll with blonde sculpted hair stands in attendance. Excellent condition. Circa 1880. $2500/3500

318. *German Wooden Grocery Store "Kolonialhandel" and Furnishings*

18"w x 9"h x 11"d. A heavy wooden store in stage-like frame with natural dark stained finish features pull-out drawers with bone handles, center name crest at the back labeled "Kolonialhandel", separate counter and wooden desk, and a number of contents, viz. multiple food boxes and packages, basket of bottles, painted wood liquor bottlers, a tin scale and a tin paper cutter. A German bisque dollhouse man serves as the grocer. Germany, circa 1890. Excellent condition. $1000/1400

319 detail.

319. German Dollhouse with Bay Window and Bathroom

27"w. x 11"h. x 13"d. A large wooden framed house in stage-like form presents two large rooms each with original wall and floor papers and column front. The sitting room has an unusual three-section bay window, and the bedroom features a bathroom closet with closing door furnished with a toilet and washstand. The furnishings include a velvet couch, 2 chairs, nice wood table, wood and metal corner table and matching chair, wooden china cabinet with lithographed trim and glass panels, wooden bed with gilded trim and canopy, gold wood cradle with tiny doll, bedside table, wooden dresser with mirror. Accessories include tin server with 2 colored glasses, painted wood telephone, painted wood tea service, soft metal table lamp, cast metal candle stick and tableware. Very good condition. Germany, circa 1910, the bay window and bathroom were luxury, and hence rare, details. $1800/2300

320.

320. Three German Bisque Dollhouse Ladies

6" (15 cm.) Each has bisque shoulder head, painted facial features, original muslin body with bisqsue lower limbs and painted shoes, two with mohair wigs, one with sculpted hair. Condition: generally excellent. Comments: Germany, circa 1890. Value Points: the ladies wear lovely antique and well detailed costumes of the era. $400/600

321. German All-Bisque Girl with Ribbon Loop Hair and Rare Wooden Chair

4" (10 cm.) All-bisque older girl has blonde sculpted curly short hair with sculpted loop at the crown for insertion of real hair ribbon, painted facial features, pin-jointed limbs, painted white stockings and fancy shoes, costume. Condition: generally excellent. Marks: k 3/0. Comments: Germany, circa 1910, included is an unusual barrel-shaped child's chair with original paint-decorations comprising green background with red and cream striping and vivid floral abstracts. $200/300

322. *Wooden Miniature Toy Shoppe and Contents*

25"w. x 11"h. x 16"d. A wooden framed shop in stage-like form with flared sides has painted green interior with white shelving on two walls, lithographed paper floor and a wooden paint-decorated store counter. The shelves, floors and walls are laden with dozens of miniature toys including 2 metal doll carriages with tiny all-bisque dolls, painted iron rocking horse, pull toy horse with leather harness, basket of felt balls, wooden birdcage with bird, 7 miniature all-bisque dolls in original knit costumes, 6 painted wood shadow boxes with miniature scenes, set of bone dominos, lambs, mini books and magazines, toy horses, wooden boats, train set and cradles, tin roulette wheel, 7 frozen Charlotte dolls, painted wood tea set, tin flying planes, carrousel, and more. Dolls are all antique, the toys are mostly antique but some newer. Excellent condition of the delightful shop, peopled with three antique dollhouse dolls. $2000/2700

323. *German Bisque Girl with Tin Carriage and Teddy Bear in Chair*

4.5" (11 cm.) An all-bisque girl has long blonde curly hair decorated with a blue hair bow, painted facial features, pin-jointed limbs, painted blue shoes, antique cotton dress and undergarments. Condition: generally excellent. Comments: Germany, circa 1920, included with the blue ribbon girl is a German tin lithographed doll carriage with stenciled designs and working wheels, and a bentwood upholstered child's chair with toy beads and working wheels containing a yellow jointed teddy bear. $200/300

324. *German All-Bisque Girl with Tin Carriage and Bisque Doll's Doll*

4.5" (11 cm.) An all-bisque doll has blonde sculpted hair in short bobbed fashion, painted facial features, pin-jointed limbs, painted stockings and tan shoes, antique dress, undergarments and cap. Condition: generally excellent. Comments: Germany, circa 1915, included is a German tin lithographed carriage with stenciled designs of children playing (the girl with a little doll), containing a tiny all-bisque doll with painted hair, jointed limbs, bare feet, from an earlier period, c. 1885. $200/300

325. *Wooden Dollhouse Blue Kitchen with Furnishings*

16"l. x 8"w. x 8"h. A small wooden framed kitchen in stage-like form features cream painted walls, black and white checkered kitchen floor and a wide curtained window at the back wall. There is a built-in turquoise blue pantry with two doors, and matching countertop and cabinets and a sink. The kitchen is furnished with a metal table, gas grill, and various blue enamelware tins, pans, dishes, bread box, and various knives, grinder, iron, towels, and other kitchenware. A German blonde haired porcelain doll in antique costume is included. Excellent condition. Circa 1910. $900/1400

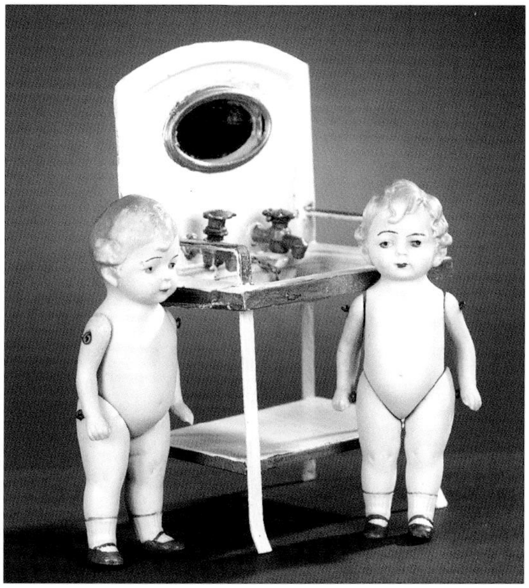

326.

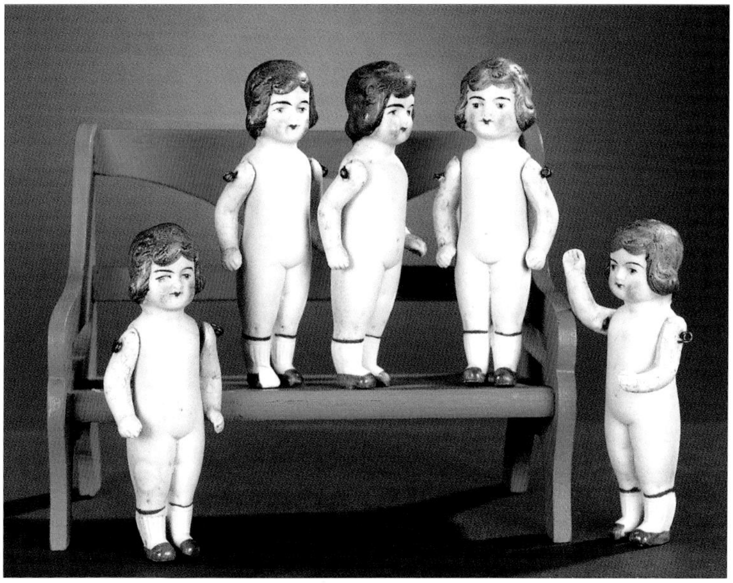

327.

326. *Pair, German All-bisque Twins with Painted Tin Bathroom Sink*

4.5" (11 cm.) 4.5" dolls. Each is all-bisque with pink tinted complexions, sculpted short brown curly hair, painted facial features, pin-jointed limbs, painted shoes and socks. Condition: generally excellent. Marks: made in Germany. Comments: Germany, circa 1920, Hertwig & Co., included is a painted white tin bathroom sink with gilded mirros and two faucets, water reservoir at the back, and sink plug with chain. $200/300

327. *German Bisque Quintuplets with Green Shoes and Bench*

3.5" (9 cm.) 3.5" dolls. Five all-bisque dolls have brown sculpted hair in short bobbed fashion, painted facial features, pin-jointed arms, painted socks and green shoes. Condition: generally excellent, one foot chipped at toe. Marks: 2/0 Germany. Comments: Germany, circa 1900, the green shoes are unusual, the dolls are posed on a German wooden dollhouse bench with original green paint. $200/300

328.

328. *Wooden Dollhouse Bathroom with Furnishings*

15" x 7"h. x 8"d. A small wooden framed bathroom in stage-like form features original paper lithographed walls, two curtained windows at the back wall and painted floor. The furnishings include a tin vanity with mirror, tin bathtub, tin toilet and toilet paper holder. There are two rubber bath mats, a celluloid bowl and pitcher, bone hair brush, and 3 all-bisque dolls. Good condition. Circa 1920. $400/600

329. *German Two-Room Dollhouse with Furnishings*

24"w. x 9"l. x 12"h. Two wooden doll rooms in stage-like setting feature three curtained windows at the back with real wooden pane frames and wide interior sills for holding plants, original flowered or textured wallpaper and original unusual pressed design floors to simulate textured wood. Furnishings include maple bedroom set with bed, marble top night stand, marble top wash stand, cupboard, marble top table, rocker and rare hanging clock with pendulum; painted red parlor set comprising settee, table, two chairs, along with parlor stove. Accessories include soft metal tea table and sewing basket, foot stool, gilded mirror, lithograph with ormolu frame, pewter dishes, bisque statue, and wash bowl and pitcher. There is a German bisque dollhouse lady included. Germany, circa 1900. $1500/1800

330. *Collection of Miniature Glass Tableware*

2" (5 cm.) 2" decanter, 31 pieces. Each of delicate blown or pressed clear glass, in a myriad of patterns, sized for dollhouse display. Included is silver-handled bucket, oval relish dish, cheese covered dish, cruet set in blown glass holders, decorative mantel pieces, pitchers, goblets, vases, and more. Excellent condition. Late 19th century. $400/500

331.

330.

331. *Early Miniature Dancing Man in Miniature Globe*

3" (8 cm.) A blown glass 3" globe with marbled paper base displays a carved wooden figure of man with sculpted and painted costume, loosely jointed legs, wire bristle legs that suspend below the wooden legs, and allow the doll to appear as though dancing. The doll was featured in Estrid Faurholt's *Book of Dolls and Doll Houses*, a beloved miniature doll in her collection. Circa 1850. $300/400

332. *German Golden Oak Dollhouse Furnishings and Dolls*

4.5" (11 cm.) doll. A massive style golden oak set is highlighted by a large cupboard that centers a matching attached settee with peach velvet upholstery and braid trim, along with four matching chairs with velvet upholstered seats, small dessert buffet, and a tall pedestal upon which is posed an earthenware bisque bust. Included is a bisque head dollhouse lady with sculpted hair, and a small all-bisque child with bobbed hair and original costume. A soft metal decanter set is included. Excellent condition. Germany, circa 1915. $400/500

333. *Petite Paper Lithographed Assembled Room with Furnishings*

10"w. x 6"h. x 8"d. A heavy cardboard folding box is permanently assembled, the box lid with richly lithographed scene visible on the underside, side and back of the room. The interior has lithographed dining room walls and floor with rich embellishments, and contains a petite set of dollhouse furnishings featuring rose silk upholstered sofa and four chairs, wooden table, potted plant, three tiny all-bisque dolls, rare early cloth doll with hand-painted features and original costume, and 2 two-panel miniature screens dated 1886. $400/600

334. *Group of German Wooden Miniatures in Original Boxes*

3" (8 cm.) wooden dolls. Included is a bent-wood box that contains two wooden carved dolls with painted costumes along with 2 wooden birds; set of tiny dollhouse furnishings with stamped transfer design of owl on the chest, still attached to original box; and three tables with inlay design on top, one in original box, with maker's label "T.H. Model Mobler". Excellent condition, unplayed with, one bird missing head. $300/400

335.

335. *Wooden Garden Room with Furnishings*

25"h. x 16"w. x 14"d. A sturdy wooden one-room cottage or garden house in original cream paint with green trim has red wooden removable roof with dormer window at the front, shaped chimney, side window, and a large front door opening for access to the paper lined interior containing woven garden furniture and tea service, a bisque doll with sculpted hair, and potted plants in the sunny doorway. Circa 1900. $500/800

339.

336. *German Wooden Dollhouse Furniture*

5" (13 cm.) Set of painted ivory wooden settee and four matching chairs are richly carved and highlighted with gilding, having original patterned silk upholstery. Excellent condition. Germany, circa 1900. $300/400

336.

337. *Group, German Metal Furniture and Accessories*

4.5" (11 cm.) 4.5" dresser with mirror. Nine pieces. Comprising furniture of soft metal with silver or gilded finish, viz. dressed with fancily bracket mirror, marble-top table with fancy base, fireplace tools, two lithographs with fancy frames, and a balloon back chair with silk seat. And objects of cast metal, viz gilded fireplace bellows, elaborate tabletop compote, high chair that converts to child's rocking chair. Excellent condition. Germany, circa 1900. $300/400

338. *Wooden Dollhouse Furnishings with Original Paper Label, and Doll*

7" (18 cm.) 7" doll. Bisque shoulder head doll with blonde sculpted hair in short curls, painted facial features, muslin body, bisque lower limbs, painted shoes, wearing antique maroon wool suit and cap. Along with 7-piece set of wooden rustic style kitchen furniture in natural finish, comprising open-front cupboard, hanging cupboard, pedestal table with paper mache tart, and four chairs, the chairs each with original paper label with illustration of a rocking horse and the marks "Bemla Leksaks Fabriks Aktierbolag". Excellent condition. Doll circa 1885. Furniture circa 1920. $300/500

339. *German Blonde Haired Porcelain Doll in Folklore Costume*

15" (38 cm.) Porcelain shoulder head, blonde sculpted hair, painted facial features, muslin body, porcelain lower arms and legs. Condition: generally excellent. Comments: Germany, circa 1910, the doll wears an antique folklore costume with heavy red wool skirt over two wool petticoats, embroidered weskit, wool jacket with braid and gold button trim, silk shawl and apron. $200/300

337.

338.

339.1. *Two All-Bisque Dolls with Puppy on Park Bench*

4" (10 cm.) 4" larger doll. Seated upon a wooden park bench is a playful trio, comprising bisque doll with painted hair and facial features, bent baby limbs,

339.1.

340.

wearing a nice antique knit costume, marked 91096' a smaller bisque naked baby with very chubby face and torso, glass eyes and sculpted brown curly hair, and a mohair puppy with black bead eyes and jointed limbs, two original German paper labels. Condition: generally excellent, puppy a bit dusty. Comments: Germany, circa 1910/1930. $200/300

340. *Small German Kitchen and Furnishings*

14"w. x 7"h. x 8"d. A small wooden kitchen in stage-like form has papered walls, two back windows with lace curtains, matching built-in corner shelf, and wooden floor. The contents include a work table and chair, various pressed tin dishes, pots, pans and utensils, hand-painted wooden bowl, wooden buckets, trays and utensils, meat grinder, and china plates. There is a black-haired china doll included. Very good condition. Circa 1910. $400/600

341.

341. *Large Pine Dollhouse with Scalloped Roof Edge*

24"w. x 21"h. x 15"d. A large pine wood dollhouse with painted black roof, white center chimney, painted pink exterior walls, set-in window frames, and unusual scalloped edge roof edging all around, has an open back for access to the large rooms. There is some old wallpaper, plain wood floors, and a built-in pine kitchen counter with sink and lid in one upstairs room. There are four five-pane windows at the front and right side, while the left side is solid. The attic roof hinges open at the back for access to one large attic room. A good early house worthy of restoration. Circa 1900. $400/600

342.

342. *Six German Bisque Dollhouse Dolls*

5-7" (13-18 cm.) Each has bisque shoulder head with sculpted hair and painted facial features, muslin stitch-jointed body, bisque lower limbs. Condition: generally excellent. Comments: Germany, circa 1900, included are two girls with painted black hair ribbons, twin ladies with brown sculpted hair, and smaller man with moustache and black boots and woman. Also included are three bisque doll heads (two reglued at neck). $300/400

343. *Group, Five German Fireplaces and Stove*

6" (15 cm.) 6" fireplace with mantel. Each is of soft metal with ivory finish and gilded or silver decoration, filigree design, each with "fire" in the fireplace, and one with an ornamental mirror above. Also included is a parlor stove with cherubic decoration. Very good condition, original finish with some paint wear, metal dents. Germany, circa 1900. $300/500

343.

344. *Small German Lithographed Parlor and Furnishings*

16"w x 8"h x 8"d. A lightwood room in stage-like form has richly detailed lithographed walls and floor with representations of lavishly curtained windows, moldings and wall paper, and contains various furnishings and accessories, viz. wooden table with four chairs and loveseat, lace area carpet, hanging gilted mirror, tin fireplace with fire and fireplace tools, gilded flower stand, gilted china closet, tin end table with floral detail, gilt 3-arm candlestick holder, glass bowl, and three framed lithographs including a delightful scene of 2 men with a horse and bow. There are three German blonde haired dollhouse china dolls included, each in antique costume. Excellent condition. Circa 1890.

345. *Group, Miniature Soft Metal Silvered or Pewter Tableware*

3" candelabra. Included is a 3-arm fancy candelabra with dark finish, four pewter plates, early style coffee pot with lid and matching creamer, cruet holer with two relish dishes and two holes for bottle (missing), pitcher urn with embossed designs, shell-shaped relish dish and small matching dishes, and a number of other miscellaneous pieces. Circa 1910. $300/400

346. *Two German Dollhouse Dolls and Rare Paper Furniture*

4" (10 cm.) The lithograph-printed dollhouse furnishings, including three chairs and a foot stool, have pressed designs, punched embroidery holes, and punched fretwork to depict rich Gothic styling; one is highlighted with red wool cross-stitch. Condition: generally excellent. Comments: circa 1880, included is a small German porcelain dollhouse lady with black painted hair, and a bisque dollhouse lady with sculpted blonde hair and black hair ribbon, each with original cloth body and bisque limbs, the china lady with fancy pink boots. $200/300

347. *German Porcelain Lady in Original Gown with Cradle, Baby and 1864 Dated Table*

6" (15 cm.) Porcelain shoulder head lady with blonde sculpted hair, painted facial features, muslin body, porcelain lower limbs, wearing blue sheer chiffon gown and undergarments. And tinplate swinging cradle with canopy top and original stenciling, containing small bisque doll, and marble top round table with pedestal base, signed on the underside "Pauline Olson, November 17, 1864". Excellent condition. Germany, circa 1870. $400/600

348. *Group, German Wooden Dollhouse Furnishings in Dark Oak*

5" (13 cm.) 5" piano. Of richly grained dark oak, the furniture includes upright piano with hinged keyboard cover, bookcase with lithographed paper back wall, two settees each with rich velvet upholstery and fringe, five matching chairs with rich upholstery, one Gothic style maple chair included. Condition: generally excellent. Germany, circa 1890. $300/400

349. *English Wooden Two-Story House with Fenced Yard and Center Staircase*

30"w x 31"h x 20"d (including yard). The heavy wooden framed house has a narrow sloping roof with extended-height roof line at each side of house with block chimney atop each, original cream paint with reddish/brown trim and dark green roof. The house features outset windows at either side of the front, that extend through both floors and terminate in a high peaked arch in front of the roof. Each front window area is three-sided with wide sills for flower pots, and there is a glass-windows front door with steepled portico. At the front of the house is a removable matching garden with faux shrubs whose fence features a swinging lattice gate. The interior features four uniform sized rooms with a center staircase and hall, each room with a built in fireplace with faux fire. The wall and floor papers are old, and partially original, There is a mirror and hall rack in the front hall. The house, from the collection of Estrid Faurholt, was featured as one of a "street of houses" in the 1965 edition of Jacob's History of Dollhouses. There are heavy cast iron handles at each side of the house for carrying. English, circa 1880. $3000/4000

350. *Two German Bisque Dolls with Playthings*

4.5" (11 cm.) 4.5" larger doll. Includes bisque dollhouse girl with blonde sculpted hair and black hair ribbon, painted facial features, muslin body, bisque lower limbs with painted orange boots, antique costume; and 4" early all-bisque with sculpted short blonde curly hair, painted facial features, peg-jointed bisque limbs, bare feet, antique costume. Included are a small bisque trinket box designed to appear as a cushion with doll and dog resting atop, and a wool plush tabby kitten with green glass eyes. Condition: generally excellent. Comments: Germany, circa 1885. $400/500

351. *Early German Dollhouse Boy with Trunk of Toys*

4" (10 cm.) 4" doll. Bisque shoulder head with black sculpted short curly hair depicting a young boy, painted facial features, muslin body, porcelain limbs, black velvet baby dress, painted fancy pink lustre boots. Condition: generally excellent. Comments: Germany, circa 1865. The little doll owns a cardboard candy container trunk with outlined straps, striped paper lining, and containing a number of miniature toys: tiny bisque doll, paper mache roly-doly, house setting, three peg-doll torsos, wooden train, rocking horse, tin lithographed tennis racquet and flannel-covered paper mache piglet. $400/500

352. *Petite German Bisque Doll with Doll Collection*

8" (20 cm.) Solid domed bisque shoulder head, painted facial features, muslin body, bisque lower limbs, black heeled boots, antique undergarments. The doll is seated upon a pair of early wooden chairs with gilded paper edging on the legs and frames, and plays with her doll collection (4 small all bisque dolls) in fancy taufling wear or basket. $300/400

End of Session One

353. *Outstanding Danish Porcelain Portrait of Queen Caroline Amalie by Royal Copenhagen*

22" (56 cm.) Pressed porcelain shoulder head with elegantly refined slender face and elongated strong throat, brown sculpted hair waved loosely over the ears into a loosely coiled nape at the back of her head, delicate stippling of hair at the neck nape, muslin stitch-jointed body, porcelain arms to above the elbows, porcelain legs with bare feet to above the knee. The doll wears a blue gown, undergarments, apron and embroidered shawl. Condition: generally excellent, repair to right toes and hairline at top of right leg. Marks: lll (with blue dot). Comments: Royal Copenhagen Porcelain manufactory, circa 1840, the doll is a portrait model of beloved Danish Queen Caroline Amalie, married to the crown price Christian who ascended to the Danish throne in 1840. $8000/10,000

354, 355.

354. *German Bisque Pouty Character "Peter" by Kammer and Reinhardt*

20" (50 cm.) Bisque socket head portraying a wistful faced child, painted facial features, pale blue eyes, closed mouth with downcast lips, brunette mohair wig, composition and wooden ball-jointed body. Condition: generally excellent, few typical wig pulls, original body and body finish. Marks: K*R 101 50. Comments: Kammer and Reinhardt, circa 1910, the doll wears his antique navy blue woolen sailor suit, cap, shoes. $3500/4500

355. *Pair, German Bisque Candy Container Dolls on Sled by Gebruder Heubach*

9" (23 cm.) Seated upon a wooden sled are two bisque head dolls with painted facial features and hair, hollow candy container torsos that separate at the waist, composition lower limbs. Condition: generally excellent, a bit surface dust. Comments: Gebruder Heubach, circa 1915, the candy container dolls wear their factory original snow suits and caps. $800/1200

356. *Petite German Bisque Child "Globe Baby" in Original Costume*

8" (20 cm.) Bisque socket head, brown glass eyes, painted facial features, slightly open mouth, teeth, blonde mohair wig, five piece composition body with painted shoes and socks. Condition: old hairline extends around throat. Marks: Globe Baby Dep CH 10/0 Germany. Comments: Carl Hartmann, circa 1910, the doll wears her wonderful antique red woolen dress and matching cap (both factory original), undergarments, and carries applique felt purse. The actual doll was featured in an article in German Doll Studies by Cieslik, (p.82) with the note "the doll factory of Carl Hartmann in Neustadt near Coburg was well known for its range of splendidly dressed 5-piece bodied dolls...clothing and accessories were the seller". $200/300

356.

357. *German Bisque Child for the Danish Market with Boutique Label*

10" (26 cm.) Bisque socket head, brown glass sleep eyes, painted facial features, open mouth, teeth, blonde mohair wig, composition ball-jointed body. Condition: generally excellent, original wig, body, body finish. Marks: Halbig K*R

357.

26. Comments: Kammer and Reinhardt, the doll's torso has original Danish doll shop label, and wears her original red woolen smock dress with yellow embroidery, matching cap, undergarments, little leather shoes signed 2/0. $400/500

358. German Bisque Boy with Sculpted Blonde Hair and Original Costume

12" (30 cm.) Bisque shoulder head with blonde sculpted hair in short boyish fashion with long bangs waved across the forehead, blue glass inset eyes, painted facial features, closed mouth, muslin stitch-jointed body, bisque lower arms, Condition: generally excellent, two finger tips chipped. Comments: circa 1880, Germany, attributed to Kling, the doll wears its original folklore costume and was featured as "Oscar" in the Legoland Museum brochures. $500/800

359. An All-Original German Bisque Doll by Kling in Original Box

15" (38 cm.) Solid domed bisque shoulder head, brown glass inset eyes, painted facial features, closed mouth with downcast pouty expression, blonde mohair wig, original muslin commercial body, bisque lower arms. Condition: generally excellent. Marks: 167-4 (doll) Gekleidete Puppen (box label meaning "dressed doll"). Comments: Kling, circa 1890, the doll is perfectly preserved in fine unplayed with condition, wearing maroon sateen and lace dress with matching bonnet, undergarments, stockings, leather shoes, and with her original red box. The doll and its costume identified as from the doll fashion house of Johannes Franz of Sonneberg and designed to capture the French doll market has been featured in articles such as Cieslik's Puppenmagazin, 1989. From the original collection of Estrid Faurholt and featured in the 1967 Book of Dolls and Doll Houses, with a story of its provenance: the doll, named Klara, was given to a little Danish girl in 1888 "with permission to take it out of the cupboard every Sunday to look at, not to play with. The little girl looked forward to this moment all week and she kept the doll until her death at the age of eighty". $1200/1700

358.

360. *Rare Danish Porcelain Doll by Royal Copenhagen with Brown Hair and Wardrobe*

12" (30 cm.) Pink tinted thick paste pressed porcelain shoulder head with sculpted brown hair in short boyish fashion, sculpted ears, painted blue eyes and facial features, blushed cheeks and chin, kid leather body, porcelain arms to above the elbows, and porcelain legs to above the knees, bare feet. Condition: generally excellent, paint rub at back of hair. Comments: Royal Copenhagen, circa 1845. The rare boy model, known in the Museum Collection as "Alex" is featured with an extensive and original wardrobe, curiously girl's costumes that comprise blue print cotton gown with cotton checkered and lace pinafore, brown woolen pinafore dress with matching jacket, green plaid woolen hooded cape with silk lining, red and white cotton striped dress with piping, red and white muslin dress, brown silk jacket, black silk cape, and an extensive number of undergarments, night caps, pinafores and night shifts. The doll was featured in Cieslik's Puppemnmagazin in 1993 in an article written by museum curator Kirsten Stadelhofer. $3500/4500

361. *Two Danish Miniatures including Engraving of Tivoli Gardens*

2" (5 cm.) Including an exquisite early engraving of Tivoli Gardens in Copenhagen, set in original frame, with Danish flag flying overhead, and 1" x 1 1/2" walnut box with slide lid, having oil-painted scene on the lid depicting a little cottage set in a grove of trees, by the side of a lake, sunset on the horizon. Excellent condition. Mid-19th century. $400/600

362. *Danish Porcelain Doll with Brown Hair and Bare Feet*

11" (28 cm.) Hand-pressed porcelain shoulder head with slightly pink tinted complexion, short brown painted hair with tousled curl onto the forehead, fully sculpted ears, painted facial features, tiny blue eyes, hint of smile, muslin body, porcelain arms to above the elbows, porcelain legs to above the knees, bare feet, wearing original blue and white cotton dress with multi-layered undergarments. Condition: generally excellent, small paint rub at back of hair. Marks: lll (inside shoulder plate). Comments: Royal Copenhagen Porcelain, circa 1845, the doll, known in the Museum as Johannes Loffler in homage to the original owner, has been featured in a number of exhibits and an article in Cieslik's Puppenmagazin. $2500/3500

363. *Danish Porcelain Brown-Haired Doll by Royal Copenhagen Porcelain*

14" (36 cm.) Thick paste pressed porcelain shoulder head with oval face and elongated throat, brown painted hair simply looped behind each sculpted ear and pulled into a coil at the back of her head, painted facial features, all kid body with shapely waist, stitched and separated fingers. Condition: generally excellent. Marks: lll. Comments: Royal Copenhagen Porcelain, circa 1845, the doll wears her original rose voile gown with delicately hand-stitched undergarments including a corset and pantalets with ties at the ankles. The doll, referred to as "Signe" while in Estrid Faurholt's collection was described by that collector as "the most finely dressed doll " that she owned. The doll was written about by Kirsten Stadelhofer in Cieslik's Puppenmagazin, 1983. $3000/4000

363.1. *Early Fruitwood Doll's Armoire*

17" (43 cm.) Of fine fruitwood with rich dark finish, the armoire features an unusual drawer at the top, having front and back dovetailing, and two paneled doors that open at the center, shaped side columns, and brass-plated metal hardware. The interior is shelved. Excellent condition. Circa 1860. $400/500

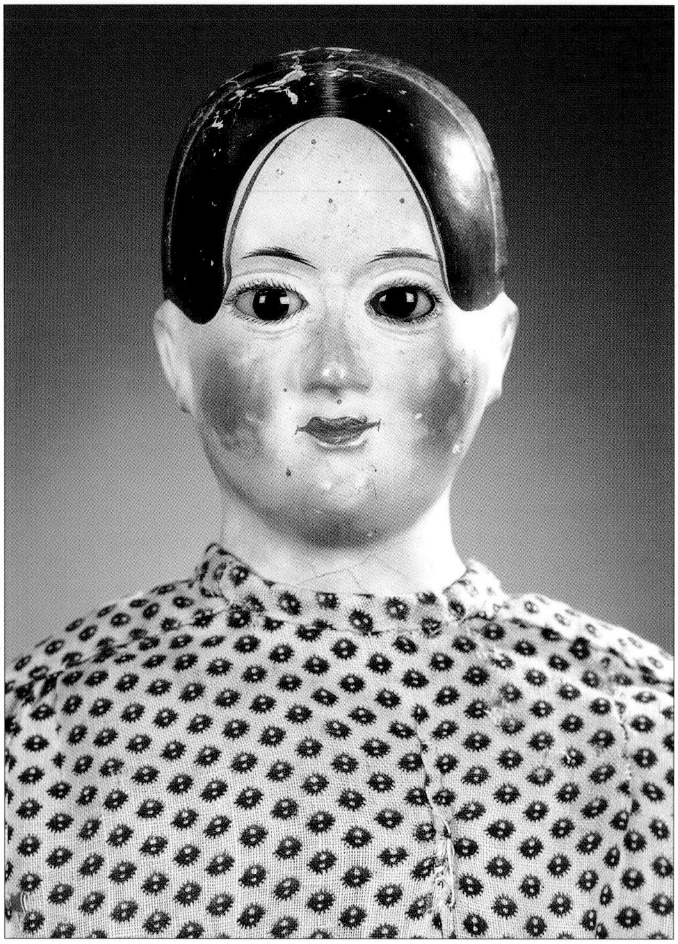

364.

365.

364. *Outstanding Early German Paper Mache Doll with Glass Eyes*

23" (58 cm.) Solid domed paper mache shoulder head with elongated strong throat and ample modeled bosom, black painted hair looping low over the sculpted ears and forming a smooth cap at the back of the head, inset large brown glass enamel eyes with unusual heavy eye lids, painted lines below the eyes lending characterization, closed mouth, blushed cheeks, muslin body with tiny waist and hefty lower torso and legs, wearing fine antique calico gown, undergarments, shoes. Condition: generally excellent, few typical paint rubs and flakes at top and back of head. Comments: circa 1840, a fine early doll with commanding presence and beauty. $2000/3000

366.

365. *Rare German Paper Mache Head with Flax and Painted Hair attributed to Muller*

4" (10 cm.) Paper mache shoulder head with unusual angled shoulder plate, modeled bosom, elongated throat, painted facial features, brown painted hair in centerpart and side parts above each sculpted ear, with attached painted flax tightly braided loop curls above each ear, and an elaborate arrangement of painted flax long looped curls at the back of the head. Condition: generally excellent, original finish and hair beautifully preserved excepting nose tip rub, and small chip on left shoulder edge. Comments: attributed to Johann Friedrich Muller, circa 1835, the hair style is based on that worn by Queen Victoria at her 1837 coronation. $800/1200

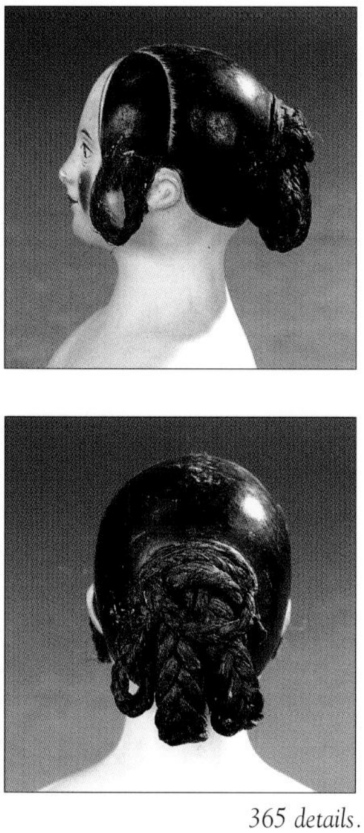

365 details.

366. *Petite Paper Mache Shell Doll with Wooden Armature*

5" (13 cm.) A paper mache doll is posed in curious manner with one arm at her side and the other held over her head, having painted hair and facial features, and wooden one piece body that is "costumed" in applied sea shells. Good condition. Circa 1860, the simple shell doll has an appealing patina and pose. $300/400

367 details.

367. *Early 19th Century Paper Mache Lady in the Rococo Style with Painted Jewelry*

14" (36 cm.) Paper mache shoulder head of adult lady with elegant slender face, elongated throat, sculpted hair in Rococo style with exaggerated roll at the back of her head, black enamel eyes, painted facial features, meticulously hand-stitched linen body with painted-over-gesso paper mache arms, and lower legs, painted white stockings and green flat shoes with ankle laces and orange ties. The doll wears her original brown velvet fitted jacket and net-over-muslin skirt, simple hand-stitched undergarments. Condition: generally excellent, original finish well-preserved. Comments: Germany, circa 1840, the doll is suggestive of the rare early Rococo series created by Muller at that time.

367, 367.1.

The aristocratic lady with unique hair has hand-painted decorative hair comb, necklace with brooch, and elaborate earrings, her body is unique and original. The doll, from the original collection of Estrid Faurholt was featured in her 1967 *Book of Dolls and Dollhouses*, page 22. $2000/3000

367.1. *Early Doll-Sized Fireplace with Engraving*

17" (43 cm.) Of cast gesso with sculpted details including dentellated edging, mantel, fireplace edging, and framing around the early engraving depicting a Watteau like scene. Very good condition, some minor chipping. Mid-19th century. $400/600

368. *Early Shell Doll "The Flower Peddler" on Original Base*

9" (23 cm.) A wax-head doll with painted facial features and wooden limbs is posed upon her original wooden stand. She wears a lavish costume made entirely of shells in a variety of colors to differentiate her blouse, skirt, apron and bonnet, and she carries a basket and bouquet of silk and shell flowers that she appears to be peddling. Included with the doll is a wooden chair with gilded paper, (very frail) silk upholstery, and shell design. Condition: generally excellent. Comments: circa 1850. $700/1000

369. *Early Paper Mache Doll with Wooden Articulated Boy and Shell Costume*

5" (13 cm.) Paper mache doll with elongated throat and black sculpted hair waved low around the sides of face and into a loosely coiled bun at the back of the head has painted facial features, all-wooden body with articulated joints, and is wearing a well-detail gown made of colorful applied shells. The doll is posed on her original base. Condition: good, old reglue at neck, original finish. Comments: circa 1840. $500/700

370, 371 details.

370. *German Porcelain Lady Doll by KPM with Early Costume*

17" (43 cm.) Thick paste porcelain shoulder head portraying slender-faced lady with elongated throat, brown painted hair in centerpart waved above the ears and smoothly capping the back of her head, painted facial features, kid stitch-jointed body, stitched and separated fingers, wearing early folklore style costume with woolen skirt, silk shawl and apron, unusual heeled wooden shoes with painted detail. Condition: generally excellent. Marks: KPM (inside shoulder plate). Comments: KPM. circa 1840, the actual doll is shown in Cieslik's German Doll Encyclopedia, page 164. The doll was featured by collector Estrid Faurholt in her 1967 *Book of Dolls and Dollhouses* wherein she noted "this girl may be in peasant dress, but she is of royal porcelain!". The Faurholt collection was the nucleus of the Legoland Museum. $4000/5000

371. *German Porcelain Lady Doll by KPM in Fine Larger Size*

23" (58 cm.) Thick paste hand-pressed porcelain shoulder head with oval face and elongated throat, brown sculpted hair loosely waved over the ears and gathered into a braided coil at the back of her head, held by a wide hair band, muslin stitch-jointed body, leather arms with stitched and separated fingers, antique gown, undergarments, shoes. Condition: generally excellent, paint ding on nose tip. Marks: KPM (below blue sceptre stamp) KPM (below a red circle). Comments: KPM, circa 1840, a fine large size with luminous complexion . $4500/6500

372. Extremely Rare German Bisque Character, 103, from the Art Character Series of Kammer and Reinhardt

23" (58 cm.) Bisque socket head with deeply sculpted characterized features of wistful older child, having blue painted eyes glancing to the right in deeply defined eye sockets, fringed upper lashes, lightly feathered brows, accented nostrils and eye corners, closed mouth with accent line between the lips, luminous glaze on bottom lip, original brunette mohair wig, original composition and wooden ball-jointed body, antique cotton dress, pinafore, undergarments, shoes and stockings. Condition: generally excellent, some typical wig pulls at back of head under wig, three fingers broken. Marks: K*R 103 58. Comments: Kammer and Reinhardt, circa 1910, from their art reform character series, few examples of this model are known to exist. The doll exhibits an extraordinary quality of sculpting including definition of cheek bones, philtrum, square-tipped nose with rounded edging, and defined temples; the bisque is exemplary. The doll has been a prominent feature in the Legoland Museum for many decades. $80,000/120,000

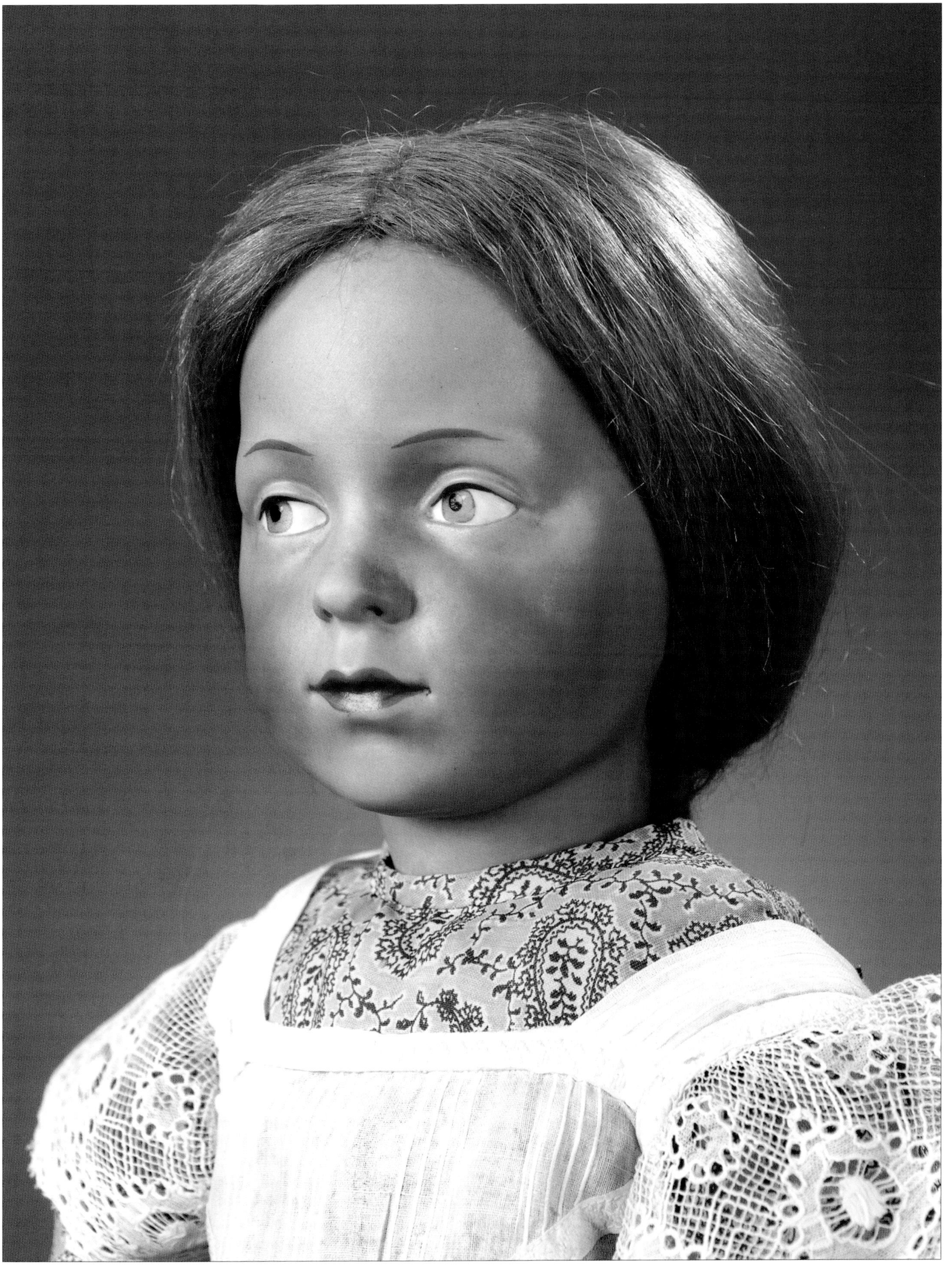

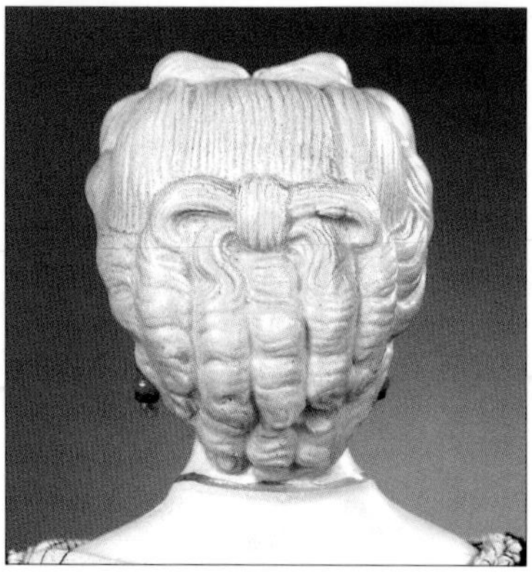

373 detail.

373. Beautiful German Bisque Glass-Eyed Doll with Glass Eyes and Modeled Necklace

22" (56 cm.) Bisque shoulder head with delicately tinted bisque having luminous patina, depicting adult woman with cobalt blue glass eyes, sculpted blonde hair with blue beaded hair comb, finger curls at the back with large hair bow, painted facial features, closed mouth, sculpted pierced ears, painted blue necklace and gold cross, slender kid body with shapely waist, stitched and separated fingers, nicely costumed. Condition: generally excellent. Comments: Germany, circa 1875, rare glass eyes and fancy modeled necklace. $1200/1500

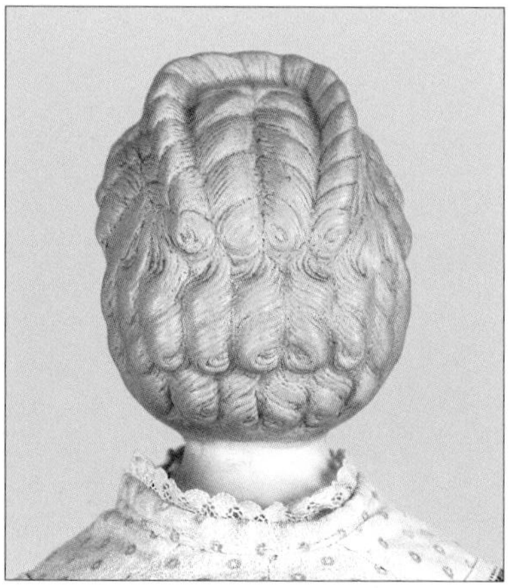

374 detail.

374. German Bisque Lady Doll with Glass Eyes and Ornately Sculpted Hair

19" (48 cm.) Bisque shoulder head portraying adult lady with slender face and elongated throat, cobalt blue glass inset eyes, painted facial features, blonde sculpted hair with three vertical arranged curls over horizontal waves at the front, crowned by a coiled braid at the crest, with arranged curls around the back, tucked behind the fully sculpted pierced ears, kid lady's body with shapely torso, antique gown and undergarments. Condition: generally excellent, some body patching. Comments: Germany, circa 1875, rarity factors include fancy coiffure, glass eyes and pierced ears. $800/1300

375. *German Bisque Lady Doll with Glass Eyes and Beaded Hair Ornaments*

375 detail.

18" (46 cm.) Pale bisque shoulder head portraying an adult lady with slender face and elongated throat, blonde sculpted hair pulled away from face into an arrangement of overall curls at the back, decorated with rows of gilded beading and held by a black hair band, fully sculpted pierced ears, cobalt blue glass eyes, painted facial features, kid body with shapely waist, one piece arms and legs, antique gown, undergarments, stockings and leather boots. Condition: generally excellent, some kid patching. Comments: Germany, circa 1875, rarities factors include ornate hair and decorations, glass eyes and pierced ears. $900/1400

376. *Remarkable German Bisque Portrait Lady with Brown Hair and Ornaments*

376 detail.

15" (38 cm.) Pale bisque shoulder head with slender face, elongated throat, brown sculpted hair waved across the top of head, the sides brushed backward in full waves that cascade into ringlet curls at each side of the throat and are captured pageboy style in a black painted snood at the back of the head; the snood is decorated with a gold band, white ribbon and four white tassels, painted facial features with distinctly upper glancing eyes, defined eye sockets, throat hollow and bosom, muslin straight-limbed body, kid arms, antique gown and undergarments. Condition: generally excellent. Comments: Germany, circa 1870, very rare model with exceptional decorations and compelling presence. $1200/1800

377. *Early Poured Wax Doll in Original Elaborate Costume*

16" (41 cm.) Honey-toned poured wax shoulder head turned to the right, blue glass inset eyes, painted facial features, closed mouth, delicate brunette mohair wig, German muslin body with waxed paper mache lower limbs, painted stockings and fancy peach boots with little heels and buttons, Condition: generally excellent. Comments: probably German, circa 1875 as indicated by wig and body style which are original. The doll wears her superb original muslin costume (a tad frail) with train and undergarments, and superb jewelry ensemble comprising watch and fob, pearl necklace with pearl dangle, pearl bracelet, and a fine pearl trimmed hair comb. $900/1300

378. *English Poured Wax Portrait Doll of Queen Victoria*

14" (36 cm.) Pink-tinted poured wax shoulder head with well defined facial features, throat hollow and cleavage, brilliant blue glass inset eyes, painted facial details, light brunette inserted hair, soft muslin body with poured wax limbs, bare feet. Condition: generally excellent, hair a bit sparse, costume delicate. Comments: English, in the Montanari style, circa 1860, the doll closely resembles Queen Victoria at the mid-19th century and is wearing her original exquisitely detailed gown, undergarments, and tiara of intertwined silk ribbons and metallic threads. The doll was from the early collection of Estrid Faurholt and featured in her 1967 *Book of Dolls and Dollhouses* described as "Victoria in Wax...an imposing personage". The Faurholt Collection later became the nucleus of the Legoland Museum. $1200/1600

378.1. *Toy Miniature Clock with Striking Gnome*

4.5" (11 cm.) Tinplate clock with silver finish over richly embossed designs featuring side columns and cherubic figural face has faux paper clock face, swinging pendulum and a figural gnome atop holding a hammer with which he strikes the gong on each hour. The minute and hour hand turn simultaneously, and the pendulum swings when keywound at back. Included is an early fruitwood table with slate top. Very good condition, the movement is sporadic. Probably French, circa 1890. $400/600

378.2. *French Cherry Wood Miniature Clock with Bronze Mounts marked A.F. Brevete*

18" (46 cm.) A beautifully shaped clock of rich cherry wood with natural finish is generously embellished with gilded cast bronze mounts, has porcelain face, pendulum with figural face surrounded by sunburst design, brass clockworks signed "A.F. Brevete SGDG 854". $2000/2500

378.3. *Early Miniature Walnut Clock with Decorated Clock Face*

17" (43 cm.) Of fine walnut finish with inlay banding, mother of pearl medallion, and urn shaped ornament at the crest, the clock features a porcelain watch face in a cast bronze mounting that features figurals of cherubs placing a crown on the profile of a person. The clock face is decorated with three oval painted colorful scenes featuring a woman's face and two cottages, and has three dials, for hourly time, for day of the month and for month of the year. Excellent condition, appears complete and working. $900/1300

378.4. *Fine Early Miniature Clock Case with Bone Inlays*

11" (28 cm.) Walnut case clock with richly banded inlays of fruitwood and bone is decorated with three ivory finials. The roof slides off to reveal a fitted interior for insertion of pocket watch. (Watch included but of later period, c.1930). Condition of case excellent with two splits in bone inlay. 19th century. $400/500

378.5. *Miniature Grandfather Clock with Watch Works*

12" (30 cm.) A wooden grandfather clock case of fine rich walnut has faux winding door, and is surmounted by three carved finials. A brass clock works is accessed at the back with winding attached key. Case is excellent, clock appears overwound. Circa 1890. $300/500

378.6. *Miniature Oak Grandfather Clock with Pocket Watch*

11" (28 cm.) Dark oak cased grandfather clock with simple style has removable lid for insertion of pocket watch. The pocket watch with minute hand and porcelain face is included. Circa 1890. Case is excellent, hairline on porcelain face, condition of watch is unknown. $300/400

378.3 detail.

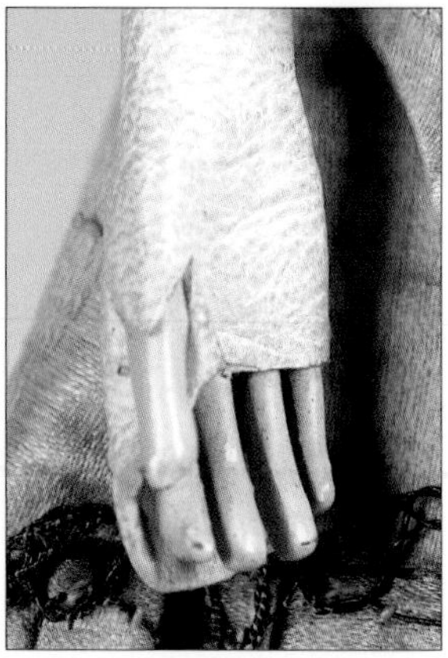

379, 380.

379 details.

379. *Fine Early English Wooden Doll Known as "Lady Elton" from the 1690 era*

13" (33 cm.) Featuring a one piece carved head and torso with wasp waist, slightly heightened bosom, shaped hips; having painted gesso on wood face, upper torso, torso and legs from waist down, and lower arms and hands, the black painted eyes having two tiny eye dots, delicately painted upper lashes, narrow stroked brows, closed mouth with primly shaped lips, and a distinctively carved nose indicated by absent nose bridge. The doll has rouged cheeks and two prominent beauty spots in addition to eight tiny dots. Her original natural hair wig is sewn to a linen cap. Her limbs are somewhat crudely dowel-jointed at the hips, knees, shoulder and elbows, and her fingers are separately carved. The doll wears a silk and muslin gown that appears to be original and matching attached slippers and muslin cap. Condition: generally excellent, finish entirely original, small nose tip rub, two tiny paint flakes on right cheek. Comments: during the late 1600's a series of dolls with remarkably similar expressions and construction details were accomplished, likely by the same English craftsman on commission for British aristocracy; the series includes the famous Lord and Lady Clapham at the Victoria and Albert Museum and this doll, known as Lady Elton. The keynote doll from the Estrid Faurholt collection was featured on the cover of her 1967 *Book of Dolls and Dollhouses*. The Faurholt Collection was later acquired by the Legoland Museum and has been a feature doll in that museum for nearly half a century. $20,000/35,000

380. *Early Painted Wooden Doll's Cupboard*

17" (43 cm.) Wooden cupboard with arched crown and double doors features two front windows of unusual shape with defined frames, carved keyholes, rounded feet, detailed shaping of base and crown, angled sides, heavy cast hinges that are painted similarly to cupboard. The verdigris-painted cupboard has pleasing soft patina and edged with a rose/cream marbled pattern. Excellent condition. Early 19th century. $2000/2500

381. *Danish Porcelain Doll "Luise Moltke" with Generous Trousseau*

18" (46 cm.) Thick paste porcelain shoulder head with oval-shaped face, elongated throat, brown sculpted hair with arranged finger curls in front of sculpted ears, and the balance of her hair drawn up into a loosely coiled arrangement at the top of her head, painted facial features, muslin body, wooden lower arms and legs. Condition: restoration to the throat and back of shoulderplate, possibly to the side of face. Comments: attributed to Royal Copenhagen, circa 1850, the doll was presented in the Legoland Museum as "Luise Moltke" in homage to her original owner, and possesses an extensive original trousseau comprising white two-piece suit, woolen patterned gown with tiny flowered pattern, night shirt and cap, purple silk gown, rose cotton gown and apron, and two exceptional evening gowns, one having an unusual decoupage of lady's head enhanced by rich embroidery. $3000/4000

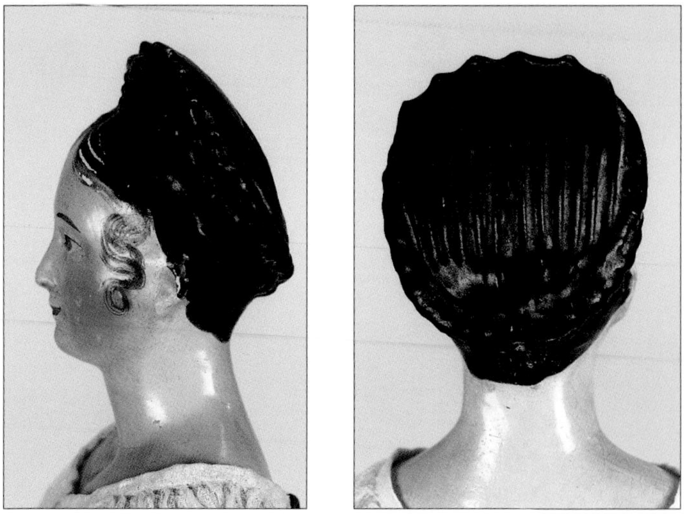

382 details.

382. *Early German Paper Mache Lady with Ornate Coiffure*

16" (41 cm.) Paper mache shoulder head portraying a woman of the 1810 era, with elongated throat, modeled bosom, oval-shaped face with painted facial features, sculpted hair with stippled details around the forehead, long tendrils of curls onto the cheeks, four rows of coiled braids in front of a decorative hair comb that forms a crown on the top of the head, original slender leather body in so-called dangling style with unique stitched hole in lower torso for stand support, stitched and separated fingers. Condition: generally excellent, beautiful original complexion, kid body original and very clean and sturdy. Comments: circa 1820, possibly Johann Friedrich Muller. $2000/3000

383. *19th Century Sewing Ephemera and Tools*

7" (18 cm.) 7"h. sewing machine. Included is an early cast iron child's sewing machine with red stenciled designs marked DRGM; eight superb doll fashion patterns for lady dolls with color tinted engravings of the costume, in original envelope dated 1875; carved bone basket as pincushion, early embroidery booklet with designs, woven basket with threads and buttons, leather necessaire with faux-ivory sewing tools. Very good to excellent condition. Late 19th century. $400/600

384. *German Softpaste Child's Dinner Service by Villeroy and Boch*

5.5" (14 cm.) 5.5"h. tureen. Of creamy softpaste, with red stenciled borders, the service has wonderful printed designs of elf-like creatures in nature settings; more then ten different designs are included. The set

comprises large lidded tureen, covered sugar, creamer, gravy boat with underplate, oval serving tray, round serving plate, large bowl, lidded coffeepot, seven saucers, six cups, and six soup bowls. Excellent condition. Marked "Villery & Boch, Wallerfanger" and "3035". Mid/late 19th century. $400/700

384 detail.

385 detail.

385. *English Softpaste Lustre Child's Tea Set*

4" (10 cm.) 4"h. teapot. Of creamy softpaste with purple lustre edging and finial, the child-sized tea set features black transfer patterns depicting two different scenes; in one scene a father and son play tug-of-war in a garden setting, while the other scene portrays a garden tea party. The set comprises a lidded teapot, sugar, creamer, and three cups and saucers. Excellent condition, sugar bowl darkened. Marked "Sewell". English, mid-19th century. $400/500

386. *A Very Rare Cast Iron Mechanical Toy "Lady at Sewing Machine"*

7" (18 cm.) Of heavy cast iron the toy features a cast figure of woman with long dress trimmed with painted ruffle, red-shoe'd feet peeking beneath the hem of the gown, short curly hair and painted facial features, jointed shoulders. She is seated behind a miniature cast iron sewing machine, holding a lever in each hand. Under her seat is a hidden spool of thread that is attached to the machine through her arm. When the wooden handled lever at the back is turned, the woman nods her head back and forth, and moves her arms as though sewing. The toy is painted its original black with gilt and aqua finish. The number "162" in impressed on the top plate of the sewing machine. Very good condition, finish original except possible touch-up on face, paint worn on her right arm and right cheek. Circa 1875. $1200/1700

387. *English Cast Iron Mechanical Bank "Dinah" by John Harper Ltd.*

6.5" (17 cm.) Of cast iron, depicting a black woman with sculpted curly hair, gold earrings and necklace and short sleeve painted green dress. When coin lever pulled, she lifts her right arm and "swallows" the coin, while her eyes blink. Excellent condition. Marked "Dinah R.No 581285". John Hancock, Ltd, England, circa 1911. $600/1000

389. *Cast Iron Mechanical Bank "Punch and Judy" by Shepard Hardware*

7" (18 cm.) Cast iron theatre with name embossed above "Punch and Judy" features those figures performing. She moves her frying pan to the right for placement of a coin, and when the lever is pushed, she quickly moves the coin to her left, while Punch waves his stick. Good condition, original finish albeit quite worn. Shepard Hardware, circa 1890. $1000/1500

388. *American Cast Iron Bulldog Bank by Stevens*

7" (18 cm.) The cast iron bank depicts a bull dog seated on a chest, a purple blanket at his seat and a thick cast iron studded "leather" collar around his neck. His tail acts as a lever for opening his mouth, tucking his head into his collar, and then "swallowing" the coin. Marked "Bull Dog Bank". Fair/good condition, tail tip and eyes missing, springs are very sluggish. J&E Stevens, circa 1890. $300/500

390. *Two Cast Iron Mechanical Elephant Banks*

7.5" (19 cm.) Each is cast iron elephant with tusks, and trunk designed to hold a coin at the tip. When tail is lifted (brown elephant) or pushed (grey elephant) the trunk lifts and feeds the coin into the slit at elephant's crown. Included is a brown elephant with red circus blanket having three embossed stars, and grey elephant with painted red riding platform and blanket. Both very good to excellent condition. Late 19th century. $600/900

391. *Cast Iron Golliwog Still Bank*

6.5" (17 cm.) Cast iron figure of the children's literary figure, Golliwog, created by the English writer/illustrator Florence Upton, having caricature facial expression and hair, wearing signature blue jacket with red trousers, large feet, With coin slit at the back torso. Circa 1890. Excellent condition, minor paint fading. $400/500

391.

392.

392. *American Cast Iron "Tammany Bank" by J&E Stevens*

6" (15 cm.) Cast iron figure of a well-fed prosperous business man seated in a red cast iron chair, wearing black business suit with yellow vest and white shirt. When coin is inserted into the slit in his hand, he feeds it "secretly" into his jacket pocket while nodding his head in an agreeable manner. The bank was an amusing stab at the nefarious backroom shenanigans of New York's Tammany political power group. J&E Stevens, circa 1875. Very good to excellent condition, original finish with some paint fading. $400/600

393. *Cast Iron Mechanical Bank "Jonah and the Whale" by Shepard Hardware*

9" (23 cm.) 9"l. Cast iron vignette depicts Jonah and friend in a small yellow boat facing a large whale on a sea of waves. When a coin is placed on Jonah's head and the lever pushed, Jonah moves forward, drops the coin in the whale's mouth that is hinged to open and close. Very good to excellent condition, some possible paint retouch. Shepard Hardware, circa 1890. $1100/1500

394. *Cast Iron Mechanical "Monkey Bank"*

8" (20 cm.) 8"l. Posed upon a cast iron green platform with embossed name "Monkey Bank" is an organ grinder; a monkey wearing yellow jacket is at the other end. When a coin is placed in monkey's mouth and the lever in base pushed, the monkey leaps forward and inserts the coin in the organ bank. Unmarked, circa 1890. Very good condition, some possible retouch. $800/1200

395. *"Always Did Spise a Mule" Cast Iron Bank by Stevens*

10" (25 cm.) Cast iron vignette portrays a black jockey in red costume and cap seated atop a mule with harness and saddle. When coin inserted and lever pulled the jockey propels forward, tumbling off the mule and falling head first onto the ground. Coin plate missing, unrestored but paint well worn, lever needs adjustment. J&E Stevens, circa 1885. $700/900

393.

394.

395.

396.

398.

396. *Five Carved Wooden Hand Puppets*

14" (36 cm.) Each having carved wooden or paper mache head with creatively designed facial expression and carved hair, hat or helmet, each with original painted complexion, hair and features, and having hollow costume with carved wooden lower arms and legs, for use as puppets with the popular children's Punch and Judy or Polichinelle theatres of the 19th century. Excellent condition, one foot missing. Circa 1880. $400/600

397. *Lot of German Accessories for School Children Dolls*

4" (10 cm.) 4"x 5" red folio. A fine group of miniature school accessories for costuming dolls about 18"-22", including red cardboard school bag with silver decorations labeled "Schul-mappe", leather double-handled back pack with fur coating, smaller faux leather back pack with slate board and notebooks, Musik folio with sheet music "The Irish Emigrant", yarn ball, mittens on a string, leather book strap with book "The Garden Door" and two maple pencil cases with sliding lids. Good to excellent condition. Early 20th century. $500/800

397.

399.

400 detail.

398. *German Bisque Pouty by Marseille with Mechanical Kitten*

11" (28 cm.) Solid domed bisque socket head with painted boyish hair and painted facial features, pouty expression, five piece paper mache body, wearing antique cotton play dress with matching pinafore, stockings, leather shoes. Condition: generally excellent. Marks: Made in Germany A M 2/0 DRGM. Comments: Marseille, circa 1910 from their rare painted eye character series, included is a tin mechanical kitten which when wound briskly moves about the floor, wagging tail, and licking the plate of milk she holds. $800/1000

399. *German Bisque Smiling Character, 640, by Marseille*

10" (25 cm.) Bisque shoulder head with blue glass sleep eye, painted facial features, closed mouth with impish smile, wig, kid jointed body, bisque lower arms, nicely costumed in antique dress and embroidered apron, undergarments, shoes and socks. Condition: generally excellent. Marks: 640 A 5/0 M Germany DRGM. Comments: Marseille, circa 1915, a rare model with pleasing expression. $600/900

400. *An Early German Lithographed Schoolroom with 26 students*

9" (23 cm.) 9"h. 19" opened d. A wooden one room school room with paper lithographed exterior and red roof, folds open at front and half of roof to form a large school room. A paper mache professor stands in front of the room whipping a pleading student on bended knees, while another student stands nearby weeping. 24 other students sit obediently at the little seats, each with a large notebook and each notebook emblazoned with a different letter of the alphabet (except y and z, presumably belonging to the two troublemakers!). Each student has vividly painted costume including modeled long hair on the boys and a colorful head scarf on the girls. A slate and lesson plans hang on the wall. Excellent condition. Germany, circa 1875, a rare and beautifully detailed early room. $2000/3000

401. *German Porcelain Tea Service with Scenes of Childhood*

5.5" (14 cm.) White porcelain tea service is decorated with colorful scenes of children at play, including cooking dinner, teaching, serving cake, washing clothes, hanging laundry, and playing see-saw. Included is lidded teapot, creamer, sugar bowl, seven cups, six saucers. Excellent condition, small chip on one cup. Germany, circa 1920. $300/500

401.

402. *Collection of Toy Pocket Watches*

2.5" diameter largest. Six toy pocket watches with embossed or gilded tin cases feature enameled or painted faces, two with closed case, and several with chains, and pair of pince-nez. Excellent condition. Circa 1900. $300/400

402.

404 detail.

403, 404.

404. *Early Miniature Slant-Front Pine Desk with Bone Inlays*

19" (48 cm.) 19"h. x 15"w. x 10"d. A pine wood slant front desk in country style has a narrow pencil drawer with notched carving above two wide drawers, each with simple dove-tailed construction, and resting upon bracket feet. The slant front opens to reveal a center cabinet with notched carving flanked by two pairs of two drawers. Carved bone knobs, inlays and faux key hole covers add decorations, and the drawers have hand-made cast brass heart-shaped pulls. Circa 1840, a very appealing and individual hand-crafted desk in well-preserved condition. $2000/3500

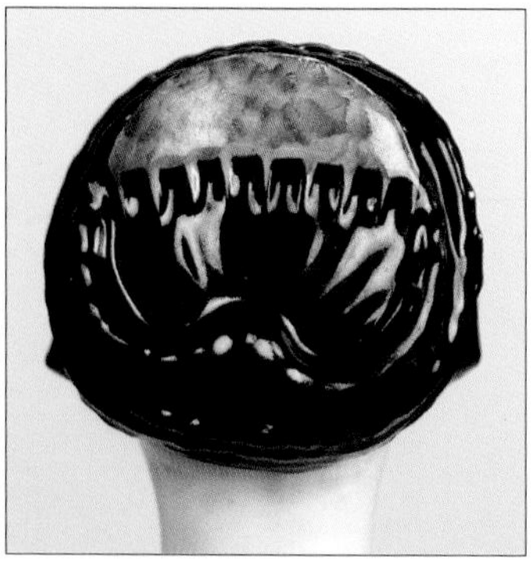

403 detail.

403. *Very Rare Swedish Porcelain Doll Attributed to Rorstrand with Superb Coiffure*

24" (61 cm.) Hand-pressed porcelain shoulder head portraying an adult woman with oval face, elongated throat, black sculpted hair waved low over the ears and then forming two extended length braids that are wrapped around the back of the head and decorated by a sculpted painted hair comb, painted facial features with refined expression, muslin body, wooden lower limbs, antique sheer muslin gown, undergarments. Condition: generally excellent, tiny early chip on right shoulderplate. Comments: attributed to Rorstrand Porcelain of Stockholm, circa 1845, few examples of dolls by this firm are known to exist. $3500/4500

405. *German Porcelain Miniature Fortune-Telling Doll*

5" (13 cm.) Porcelain shoulder head with pink tinted complexion, black sculpted hair loosely waved to back of head chignon, painted facial features. The doll's torso is attached to a "skirt" formed of folded paper fortunes, and she wears her original jacket and turban. Condition: generally excellent. Comments: Germany, circa 1850, the fortunes are presented in German, French and English languages. $600/900

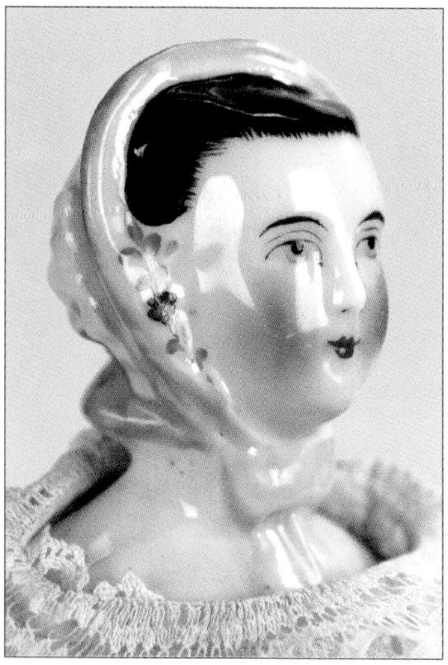

406. Rare Petite German Porcelain Doll with Blue Bonnet and Yellow Streamers

12" (30 cm.) Porcelain shoulder head with black sculpted hair waved away from forehead and captured under a blue bonnet with wide brim, delicate clusters of flowers above each ear, and wide yellow bow under the throat and on either side of the back of bonnet, stippling detail of hair at forehead, painted facial features, blushed cheeks, old leather body with tiny waist, wearing antique muslin gown and undergarments, red leather slippers. Condition: generally excellent, small very old flake at back bonnet rim. Marks: 2/0 (inside shoulder plate). Comments: Germany, circa 1870, the doll came from the early collection of Estrid Faurholt and was featured in her *Book of Dolls and Dollhouses* before moving to the Legoland Museum. $800/1200

407. Superb Early Miniature Canopy Walnut Bed

18" (46 cm.) A fine doll's bed is of walnut with burled inlays, richly carved posts, and a well-turned canopy with early blue fabric fringed curtains. The bed is fitted with generous mattress and bed linens upon which is resting a German black haired china doll in night shirt, with her breakfast tray that includes early porcelain plate, napkin ring and a hallmarked silver spoon. Excellent condition. Bed circa 1860, doll circa 1885. $1200/1800

408. Extremely Rare Carved Wooden "Surprise" Doll

5.5" (14 cm.) An all wooden doll depicts a brown-robed monk with carved costume details, painted gesso over wood face and hair. Although the body appears as one piece, the upper and lower bodies can be separated, and when done, the lower body unhinges to form a three part arched stage depicting scenes of the Mass. The scenes are minutely painted with details of clock, windows, altar, pews, and tiny priest. Condition: generally excellent, some wear to facial paint, interior painting and vignette are perfectly preserved. Comments: Germany, circa 1850. $1200/1700

408 detail.

410, 411, 412, 413.

409. *German Bisque Half-Doll Portraying Old Woman with Scarf*

3" (8 cm.) One piece bisque figure depicting an aged woman, modeled from the waist up and designed for use as pincushion form, the woman having a sculpted head scarf and blouse, her hands held clasped in front of her body, and finished in soft sepia tones. Condition: small flakes on underside of bottom edge, otherwise excellent. Comments: Germany, circa 1910. $200/300

410. *German Porcelain Doll with Sculpted Mauve and Gilt Tiara and Earrings*

12" (30 cm.) Porcelain shoulder head with black sculpted hair arranged with one long looped curl behind each sculpted ear and then drawn into tightly braided chignon at back of head, the hair topped by a curved-top tiara painted mauve at the back and gilded at the front, sculpted drop earrings, painted facial features, bisque lower arms and legs, painted boots, nicely costume in early cotton gown, undergarments. Condition: generally excellent. Marks: 0. Comments: Germany, circa 1865, from the original collection of Estrid Faurholt who noted "we know that this grand dame has never washed a doll dish in her life" in her *Book of Dolls and Dollhouses*. $800/1000

411. *German Bisque Doll with Fancily Sculpted Black Coiffure*

11" (28 cm.) Porcelain shoulder head with black sculpted hair drawn away from face into two wide poufs at the sides, with looped wide page boy curl at the back topped by a narrow braid, stippling detail at the forehead, painted facial features, early kid body with shapely torso, separated fingers, wearing antique cotton gown with detachable cape collar, undergarments, velvet slippers. Condition: generally excellent, some rubs to hair paint at back of head. Comments: Germany, circa 1865. $700/900

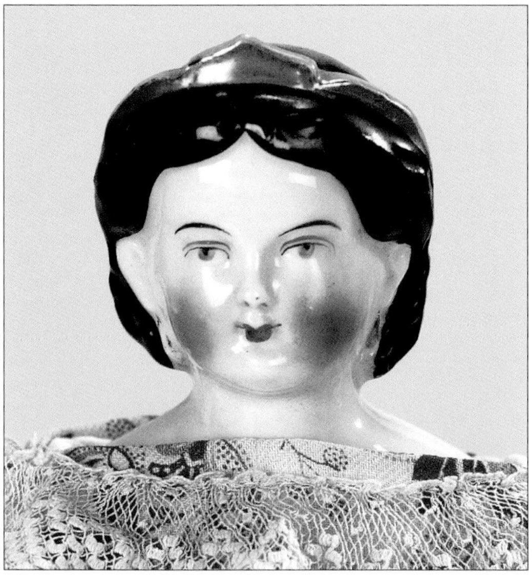

410.

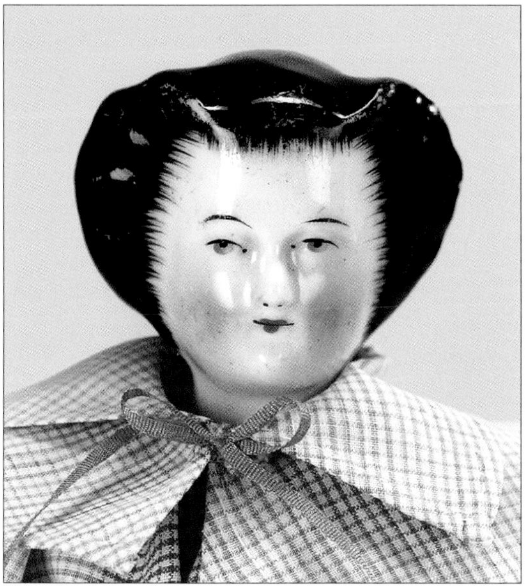

411.

412.

413.

412. Early Miniature Cabinetmaker's Secretary Desk of Rich Fruitwoods

18" (46 cm.) A beautifully styled desk made with the hand of a fine cabinetmaker, featuring dove-tailed construction of drawers and finely executed inlay designs. Of rich cherry or walnut with maple interior and columns, the desk features a steepled crest, and nicely shaped legs and apron, roll-top front of one-piece curved wood, interior drawer with star-shaped and garland inlay, and various pencil-stripe inlays on the exterior. There is a cupboard top with opening doors and two lower drawers, each with carved bone knob (one tip missing). Excellent condition. Circa 1850. $1200/1800

413. Early Miniature Tilt-Top Inlay Table with Statuary

4" (10 cm.) A fine walnut pedestal table with very fancy carved base and curved paw legs features a six-sided table top with intricate star-shaped inlays of four different woods; the table has release hinge on the underside so it can be displayed in tilt-top style when not in use. Included are 5 German miniature bisque figurines of the same era. Excellent condition. Circa 1880. $800/1000

414. Four Early Carved Ivory Cases

4.5" (11 cm.) 4"h. largest. Each is of finely carved ivory or bone including three calling card cases with removable lids, and one rosary case with slide lid; the three largest with an intricate carving of Chinese scene on either side. Excellent condition, largest has a repair on lid. Mid-19th century. $400/600

415. *Early German Porcelain Doll with Brown Hair and Maker's Mark*

14" (36 cm.) Pink-tinted thick paste shoulder head with very slender face and elongated throat, brown sculpted hair looped in front of the beautifully sculpted ears and forming a tightly braided chignon at the back of the head, painted facial features with fine detail of tapered shape brows and accented lips, kid body with shapely waist, separate thumbs, stitched fingers, lovely antique cotton gown and undergarments including a warm red wool petticoat, leather shoes. Condition: generally excellent, paint rubs at nose tip and back of chignon. Marks: (3 dots and line in green stamp inside shoulder plate). Comments: circa 1845, a beautiful early lady with refined poised expression. $1200/1700

416. *German Porcelain Doll with Ornately Arranged Chignon in Petite Size*

10" (25 cm.) Pink-tinted porcelain shoulder head with loosely sculpted black hair in wide loops at the sides of head, covering the ears, and forming a tightly braided chignon at the back of her head, painted facial features, kid body with wooden limbs and painted flat shoes, lovely antique cotton gown and antique undergarments. Condition: generally excellent. Comments: Germany, circa 1845. $600/900

417. *German Porcelain Lady Doll with Unusual Large Eyes*

15" (38 cm.) Porcelain shoulder head with deeply sloping shoulders, slightly modeled bosom, and oval shaped face, black sculpted hair with unusual combmark details looped loosely over her ears and pulled into a braided chignon at the back of her head with defined decorative comb edging, painted facial features with unusually large blue eyes, muslin stitch-jointed body, wooden lower arms, early gown and undergarments. Condition: generally excellent, right wooden thumb missing, some typical paint rubs in hair. Comments: Germany, circa 1850. The doll was an important aspect of the original Estrid Faurholt Collection, later acquired by the Legoland Museum, who described the doll in her *Book of Dolls and Dollhouses* as "her eyeballs protrude slightly, making her gaze a candid one." $800/1200

418.

418. *German Porcelain Lady with Early Coiffure and Richly Painted Lips*

21" (53 cm.) Porcelain shoulder head with oval-shaped face and elongated throat, modeled cleavage, lightly pink tinted complexion, black sculpted hair loosely looped over each ear with defined hair waves, and drawn into a tightly braided chignon at the back of head decorated by sculpted comb, painted facial features, well defined eyes, richly painted outlined lips, muslin/kid stitch-jointed body with crudely defined fingers, black silk costume. Condition: generally excellent. Marks: 6 (or C, scroll inside shoulderplate). Comments: circa 1850, an identical coiffure to #417 with distinct variations in facial model and painting. $1100/1800

419. *Early English Softpaste with Country Home Scenes*

3" (8 cm). 3"h. tureen. The oval lidded tureen of rich creamy hand-pressed softpaste features a deep cobalt blue transfer design with country home, fence and horses on one side, and a meadow with bridge and cows on the other. There are two matching oval platters (each with old flake on underside of rim.) English, circa 1865. $200/300

420. *German Porcelain Lady with Braided Chignon*

18" (46 cm.) Slightly pink tinted porcelain shoulder head with oval face, elongated throat, black sculpted hair loosely looped over the ears and ending in a tightly braided chignon at the back of her head, painted facial features, muslin body (recovered), porcelain lower arms, antique gown and undergarments. Condition: generally excellent, right hand restored. Comments: Germany, circa 1860, an identical coiffure to the preceding lot with less hand-pressed detail. $800/1000

421. *English Soft Paste Children's Dishes by Davenport*

420.

5" (13 cm.) 5"diam. dinner plate. Of white soft paste with unusual mauve or lavender transfer floral and garland decorations, the service comprises two lidded tureens with underplates and ladle cut-outs, large square covered serving dish, two oval vegetable dishes, boat-shaped oval bowl, square bowl, gravy boat and six dinner plates. Condition: very good, few darkened, few minor rubs or flakes. Marks: Davenport (and anchor impressed mark). Comments: Davenport, English, circa 1870, an unusual color of decoration. $400/500

422. *Early Chinese Exportware Children's Dishes and Bone-Handled Cutlery*

6" (15 cm.) 6"l. largest platter. 28 pieces. Of very creamy softpaste, hand-pressed as indicated by varying thicknesses, the dishes each depict two Chinese boys at play with kite in a Chinese garden, in rich blue/black designs on cream background. Included are three platters of graduated size (1 with hairline), 2 handled serving plates, 2 handled bowls, 9 dinner plates, 6 smaller plates (chip on one), 4 various bowls, and two covered tureens (small flake on inner rim of larger). Condition: generally excellent, a few pieces darkened, see notes above. Marks: (Chinese stamped insignia). Comments: mid-19th century a rare signed export set with delightful design. Also included is a wooden cutlery tray containing a number of pewter and bone-handled cutlery of which a fine carving knife marked "made in Germany", and another larger knife inscribed "P.H. & G." $500/800

421.

422.

423. French Bisque Automaton "Troubadour with Mandolin" by Roullet & Decamps

20" (51 cm.) Standing on a (worn) velvet covered platform is a bisque-head doll with brown paperweight eyes, closed mouth, blonde curly mohair wig, bisque hands, holding a wooden mandolin. When wound, and lever released, the Troubadour plays musical tunes, strums the mandolin and turns his head proudly from side to side and nods. Condition: generally excellent, some costume wear. Marks: Depose Tete Jumeau Bte SGDG 3. Comments: Roullet & Decamps, circa 1890, the doll wears a superb original velvet and silk costume with metallic edging, matching cap. $5500/7500

424. French Bisque "The Lady Troubadour" by Roullet & Decamps

20" (51 cm.) Standing on a (worn) velvet covered wooden box is a bisque-head doll with blue paperweight eyes, closed mouth, blonde mohair fleecy wig, bisque forearms, holding a wooden mandolin in her arms. When wound and lever released, music plays and she strums the mandolin, turning her head from side to side and then nodding. Condition: generally excellent, costume is all original but silk is quite worn. Marks: Depose Tete Jumeau Bte SGDG 3. Comments: Roullet & Decamps, circa 1890, a beautiful companion lady to #423 with superb original costume indicating original luxury commission. The pair were featured in Estrid Faurholt's *Book of Dolls and Dollhouses*, from her collection, and later acquired by the Legoland Museum. $5500/7500

425. Group, 19th Century Carved Bone Sewing Accessories

3" (8 cm.) 4"l. largest needle folder. Each of exquisitely carved bone, the group comprises two bone needlecases with silk lining and flannel pin holders (one is its original leather case), 2 miniature wheeled carts with velvet pincushions, and five other various sewing tools or accessories. Excellent condition. Mid-19th century. $500/700

426. Group, Early Carved Bone Miniature Toys or Play Accessories

5" (13 cm.) 5"x 5" Traveller's Set. Included is a checkers set in original box labeled "The Travellers Set Ivory Draughts" with illustration on the lid of man and woman in coach playing draughts, intricately carved Chinese fretwork box with fretwork puzzles inside, another carved box with gilded decoration and geometric puzzles inside, a set of miniature dominoes inside a container, and two roulette wheels each with carved ivory or bone pointing finger. Excellent condition. Circa 1875. $700/900

427. Three Antique Accessories for French Dolls

3" (8 cm.) 3"l fan. Included is very delicate fretwork wooden folding fan with painted designs on the

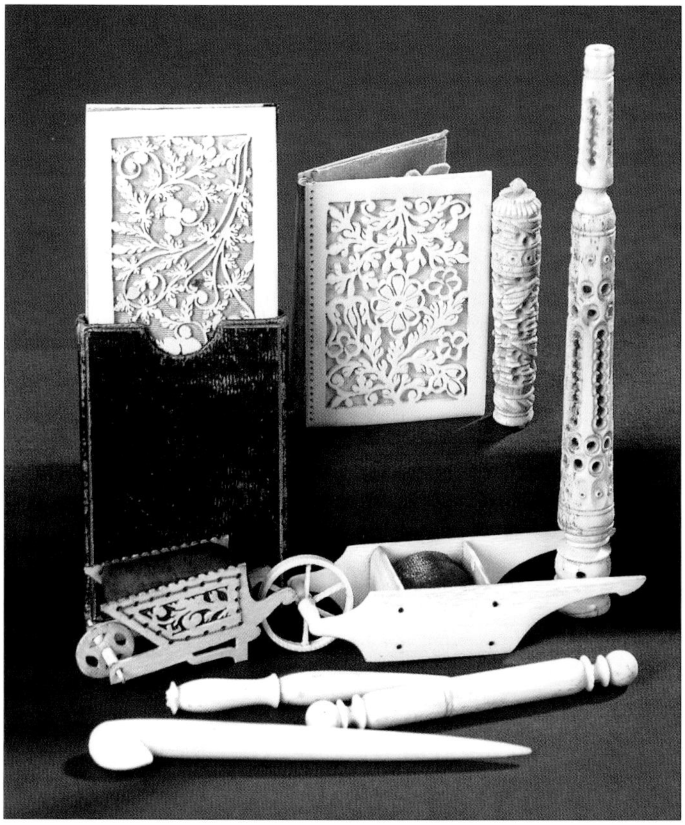

425.

426.

427.

paper liner and wooden slats, feathered tips and silk tassel on gilded belt loop; gilded metal perfume bottle as richly ornamented urn; and a heavy paper board sewing necessaire with embossed designs on exterior and tiny sewing accessories inside: gilded thimble, scissors and penknife, and bone awl, thimble and needle case. Very good to excellent condition. Circa 1875. $400/500

428. Very Beautiful French Bisque Bebe by Bru with Labeled Body

22" (56 cm.) Pressed bisque swivel head on kid-edged bisque shoulder plate with modeled bosom, blue glass paperweight inset eyes, painted facial features, closed mouth with tiny tongue tip, pierced ears, brunette mohair wig, cork pate, original kid gusset-jointed body, kid-over-wooden upper arms, bisque forearms, the doll is dressed in antique purple silk double-breasted coat dress, undergarments, matching bonnet, stockings, and shoes. Condition: generally excellent, except bisque hands are not original (appropriately sized but likely Kestner). Marks: Bru Jne 8 (head and shoulder plate). Comments: Leon Casimir Bru, circa 1882, the beautiful early model has especially clean and sturdy body with original Bru paper label. $14,000/17,000

429. *Wonderful Large German Bisque Pouty by Gebruder Heubach*

28" (71 cm.) Pink tinted bisque socket head, brown glass sleep eyes, mohair lashes, painted facial features, closed mouth with pouty expression, blonde mohair wig, composition and wooden ball-jointed body, antique costume comprising rare sharkskin double-breasted coat, jacket, pants, striped stockings, leather boots. Condition: generally excellent. Marks: 7246 12 Heubach (sunburst mark) Germany. Comments: Gebruder Heubach, circa 1912, a rare large size with very fine quality of bisque and painting, great costume. $2500/3500

430. *Collection of Toy Musical Instruments*

10" (25 cm.) 10"diam. largest drum. Included are three large toy drums, one with lithographed design of child's parade, along with two wooden drum sticks; smaller drum with wooden sides, unusual accordian-horn with pipes, and two toy horns. Good to very good condition. Late 19th century. $500/700

431. *Two Rare French Tin Lithographed Whistle Penny Toys*

4" (10 cm.) 4"l x 2.5"h. dog. Included is a gilded tin whistle with a performing dog posed upon a street organ decorated with bright colors, and a gilded tin whistle with monoplane and propeller; when the whistles are blown the dog dances and the propeller turns. Good/very good condition, object missing from side of organ. Each marked "Depose E.C." French, circa 1910. $400/600

432. *Delightful German Bisque Googly, 221, by Kestner*

15" (38 cm.) Bisque socket head, large brown glass side-glancing googly sleep eyes, closed mouth with impish smile, painted facial features, brown human hair bobbed wig, composition ball-jointed toddler body, cotton romper suit. Condition: generally excellent, tiniest flake on bottom of neck socket. Marks: G made in Germany 11 JDK 221 Ges Gesch. Comments: Kestner, circa 1910, the googly has beautiful bisque and expression, original body and body finish, carries an ABC tin lithographed toy horn. $4500/6500

433. *German Tin Lithographed Toy Music Box with Organ Music*

6" (15 cm.) Tin lithographed box in the shape of a cathedral with well defined architectural features such as leaded glass windows contained within a music box that plays church organ music when the wooden handle at the rear is turned. Marked "USA Pat.Nr1672426, DRP nr469938, DRGM Made in Germany". Excellent condition, works well, lithography bright and fresh. Circa 1910. $400/600

434. *German Lithographed-over-Wood Music Box*

10" (25 cm.) 10"w. x 5"h. A light wood box is richly covered with colorful lithographed paper depicting scenes of children's parade or children dancing in the park, while on the back side is a large circus pipe organ. Music plays when handle is turned. An original paper tune label on the bottom has pencil script tune name of "Allis Neu Machf des Mai". Excellent condition, porcelain knob missing on handle tip. Germany, circa 1900. $400/500

435. *Four German Tin Penny Toys*

3" (8 cm.) Three toys are tinplate including woman with child in carriage with lithographed designs; coffee grinder with turning handle, drawer and embossed coffee designs; unusual early washing machine with turning handle, and a heavier tin metal phonograph with horn. Good condition, some paint wear. Germany, circa 1910. $500/700

432, 433, 434.

435.

436, 437.

436. English Optical Toy "Kinora" with Nine Flip Reels

12" (30 cm.) 12"l of base. An elegant maple stand with inlay design supports a tin viewing form with apparatus for holding photographic flip reels, and a wooden turning handle. When the handle is turned the tiny photographs quickly flip creating an illusion of movement, an erstwhile early form of cinema. Included with the Kinora viewer are ten original reels; eight are in original labeled reel boxes and some have hand-lettered names of the reel: Pardow Picture (woman making herself up),Burglar, Man and wife, Railway line, and High Jump. English, circa 1895, the rare optical toy is considered an important predecessor to the cinema. Excellent condition of viewer and reels, boxes worn. $800/1200

437. German Bisque "Jubilee Googly" by Hertel and Schwab

15" (38 cm.) Bisque socket head, brown glass sleep and side-glancing eyes, closed mouth with impish smile, painted facial features, blonde mohair wig, composition ball-jointed toddler body, nicely costumed. Condition: generally excellent. Marks: 165 5. Comments: Hertel and Schwab, their Jubilee Googly, circa 1914, with excellent bisque and expression, original body and body finish. $3500/5500

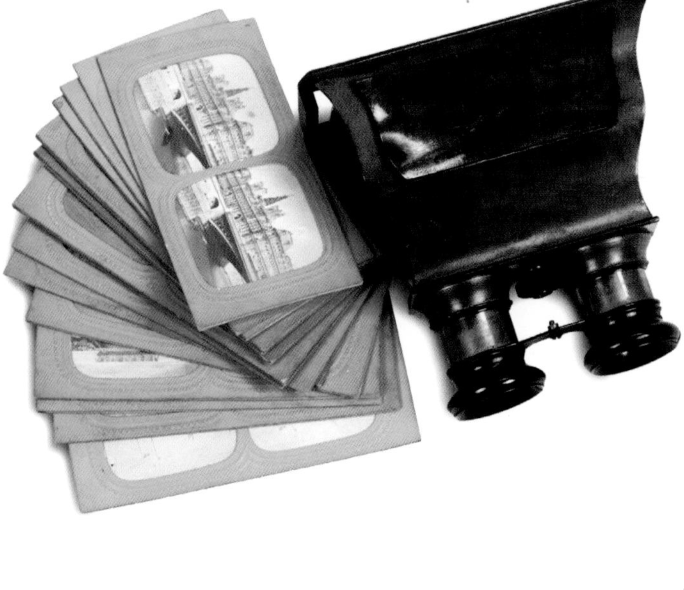

438. French Burled Walnut Peep-Show Viewer with Day/ Night Images

7" (18 cm.) 7"l. A beautiful wooden viewer of fine burled walnut with brass and copper trim allows for a series of photographs to be seen as in daylight or nightlight. Each slide is a double sepia photograph with handmade cut-outs or pinpricks on the reverse tissue side. When the slide is inserted into the viewer, and the top lid lifted or closed, the scene appears alternately as day or night. Included are 18 original views, mostly of Paris scenes including Opera, Place du Carousel, Place de la Bataille, and Louvre. Viewer excellent, scenes very good to excellent. French, circa 1880. $500/800

439. *German Bisque Googly by Walther & Sohn*

10" (25 cm.) Bisque socket head, blue glass side-glancing googly sleep eyes, closed mouth with smug expression, painted facial features, blonde mohair wig, composition ball-jointed body, antique costume. Condition: generally excellent. Marks: 208-7/0 GW (intertwined) made in Germany. Comments: Walther & Sohn, circa 1920, a rare model of the popular googly. $600/800

440, 441, 442.

440. *A Rare All-Bisque Googly by Hertel and Schwab*

12" (30 cm.) Solid domed bisque head with modeled forelock and side curls, brown glass googly sleep eyes, painted lashes, closed smiling mouth, bisque baby torso with kid-edged neckline, loop-jointed bisque bent baby arms and legs, bare feet, well-detailed antique costume. Condition: generally excellent. Marks: 172 1(head) 118 10 (inside all limbs). Comments: Hertel and Schwab, circa 1915, a very rare all-bisque version of the delightful googly. $2000/2500

441. *Fancy Wooden Baby Doll Bed with Canopy*

32" (81 cm.) 32"h x 22"l. A baby bed with reddish dark finish has fancy spindled sides, head and foot board, and a high 32" canopy at the headboard with pinwheel-shaped finials; the bed is richly fitted with mattress, sheets, linens and pillow and canopy cover having matching cutwork edging. Excellent condition. Circa 1890. $400/500

442. *A Trio of Swiss Singing Birds in Gilded Cage*

11" (28 cm.) A metal bird cage with bronzed finish and carrying loop handle contains three colorful feathered birds. When keywound, the blue bird on the perch begins to flutter feathers, turn head and sing; when the blue bird pauses the yellow bird begins its performance, and then back to the blue bird. The red bird does not sing or perform. Very good condition. Swiss, likely Reuge, circa 1940. $700/900

444. *Early French Sand Toy Known as "Tharinieres"*

6" (15 cm.) 6"h. x 5"w. A heavy card-paper closed box with black paper cover and glass front window exhibits a colorful scene of hand-tinted engraving in which a woman is feeding chickens in the farmyard. Her right arm is hinge-attached to her torso, and when sand mechanism is working she moves her arm up and down as though actually tossing the feed she holds in her apron. Condition: box and scene are well preserved with vivid colors. The sand requires an adjustment for proper movement. Comments: identical examples have been found with the Tharins paper label, French, circa 1850. $500/900

443. *An Early Paper Mache Surprise Doll in Original Box with Accessories*

9" (23 cm.) 9"h. x 6"w. A heavy card-board box with embossed paper cover and rich gilded decorations has a stage-like window at the front, exhibiting a paper mache woman with sculpted black hair, wooden hands and original costume who is standing behind a green flocked table that contains a lidded blue box and two milk glass cups and saucers. When the box is turned upside down it appears that the same scene is shown, except that now there are two glass decanters and two goblets on the table, rather than the cups and saucers. The magic trick is that there are actually two paper mache heads with identical costumes, and two blue boxes; the entire scene is changed although it appears to be only the tableware. Condition: interior scenes are excellent and perfectly preserved, the box is somewhat worn and the lid is quite worn. French, circa 1850, a very rare and delightful toy. $900/1300

445. *German Paper Mache Lady Doll*

14" (36 cm.) Paper mache shoulder head with long black sculpted hair in long finger curls low onto the back shoulders, sculpted ears, painted facial features, muslin body with tiny waist. Condition: generally excellent, original finish is well preserved. Comments: Germany, circa 1850, the early doll with rare coiffure wears a lovely antique gown of re-embroidered tulle, undergarments. $400/600

446. Early French Wooden and Paper Mache Tumbling Toy

9" (23 cm.) A wooden box with decorative stamped paper covers in a variety of pleasing designs is designed with balancing table on top of which is posed a figure representing a Chinese acrobat with paper mache head, wood limbs, cloth costume.When the box is placed in various poses, the acrobat appears to be performing various acrobatic and balancing acts. Condition: very good with original papers and decorations well preserved. Comments: French, circa 1840. $1200/1700

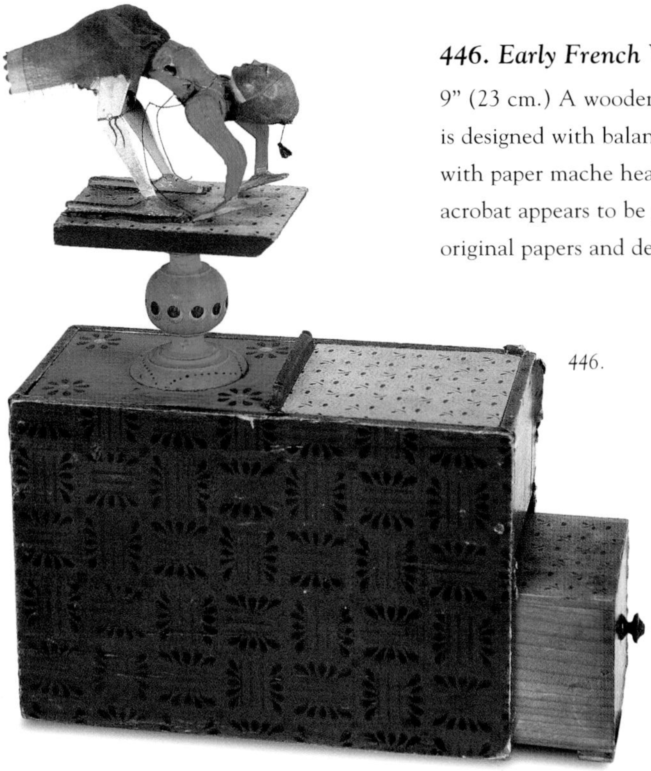

446.

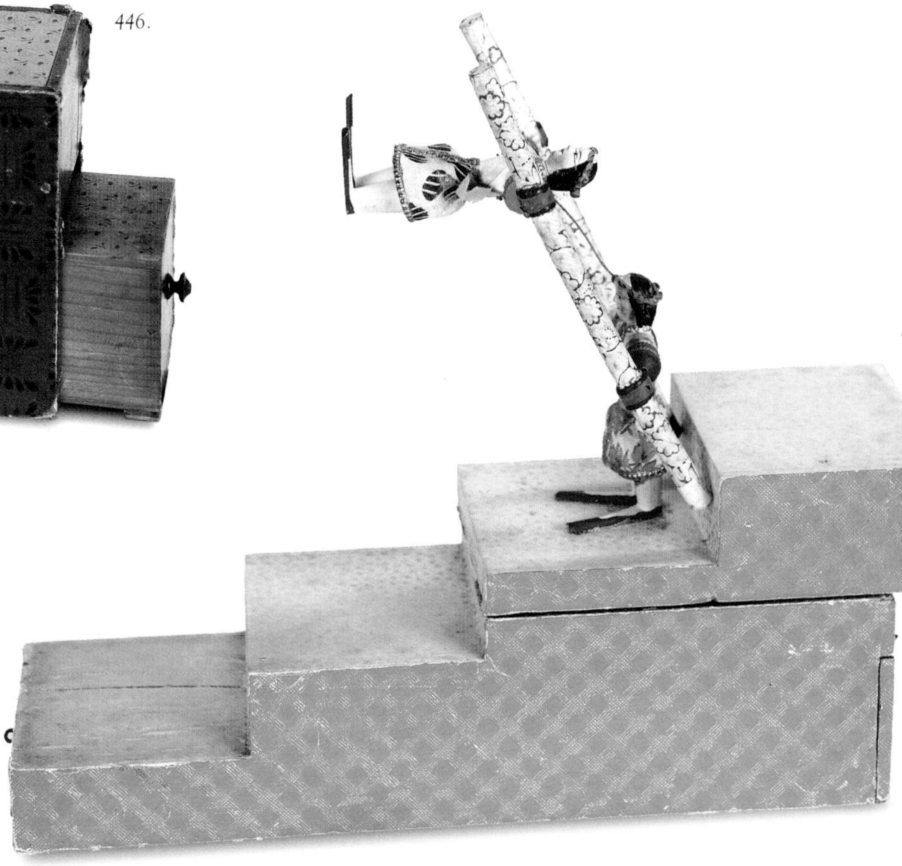

447.

447. Early French Wooden and Paper Mache Two-Figure Balancing Toy

10" (25 cm.) 19" overall 3" figures. A wooden block box that unhinges to form a series of steps, or stands upright to form a tall multi-level platform has original cream and patterned green paper cover, and supports two paper mache acrobats with painted hair, facial features, decorative garlands in hair, cloth costumes and oversized feet with painted shoes, that are posed holding onto two long cloth-covered poles. When the block is arranged in different manners, the acrobats perform various balancing or acrobatic acts. Condition: excellent, perfectly preserved. Comments: French, circa 1840. $1500/2000

448. German Paper Mache Lady Doll with Rare Coiffure

20" (51 cm.) Paper mache shoulder head of adult lady with very ornate coiffure having wide pouf curls at the sides and at the crown decorated by a hair comb, painted facial features, rarer brown eyes, early muslin body with only lower red kid arms that are simply sewn to the sleeves of the gown. Condition: very good, original finish very well preserved with one nearly invisible touch-up at back of head. Comments: Germany, circa 1830, the doll wears her original (albeit frail and mended) ivory silk satin wedding gown. From the original collection Estrid Faurholt, later acquired by Legoland Museum, the doll was shown in Faurholt's *Book of Dolls and Dollhouses* with the comment that the following note was pinned to the dress of the doll, "said to be portrait doll of Queen Victoria's mother, the Duchess of Kent". $900/1400

449. *English Early Mechanical Dancing Doll with Original Labels of Perry & Co*

11" (28 cm.) A wooden box with green paper cover contains a keywind mechanism that activates the paper mache and wooden dancing figure that is posed on the lid via a thin metal rod. The doll, with rich ebony black complexion and painted facial features has loosely wired wooden limbs, and when the toy is wound, the doll appears to dance about. Condition: very good, mechanism functions well, some craquelure to face, costume dusty. Marks: Perry & Co London...(paper label on base). Comments: England, Perry & Co, circa 1880, the dancing doll was a popular toy of the 1875-1890 era, with at least 5 different firms, mostly American creating different variations. The English version is quite rare, and includes the original paper label inside the box detailing instructions for use. $1200/1800

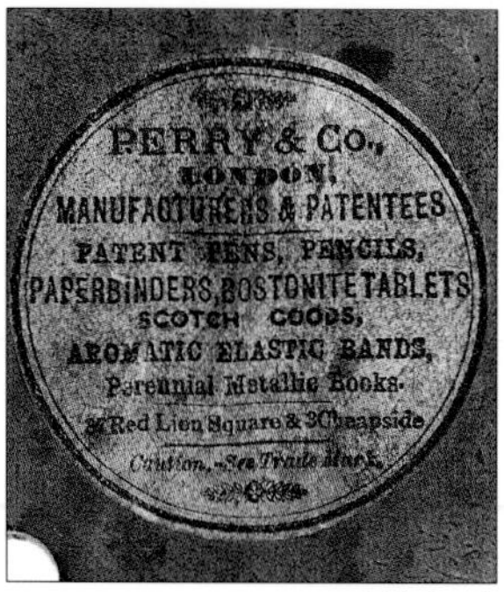

449 detail.

450. *American Clockwork Toy "Autoperipatetikous" with Original Costume*

10" (25 cm.) A German black haired china head is attached to a uniquely designed body with carton torso that forms into a cone-shaped skirt enclosing the walking mechanism, circular wooden base at hem of skirt with brass feet below. When wound the doll appears to walk about. Condition: generally excellent. Marks: Patented July 15, 1862.(stamp on base). Comments: patented by Enoch Rice Morrison, the toy was created by Martin & Runyon, circa 1865, and is wearing its original wonderfully preserved red woolen gown with lace trim. The label has the additional cautionary note "this doll is only intended to walk on a smooth surface". Included is a box fragment from the English version of the toy, with illustrations and directions. $1200/1700

450.

451. *German Porcelain Doll Portraying a Boy*

12" (30 cm.) Porcelain shoulder head with short black sculpted curly hair with detailed stippling onto the forehead, painted facial features, muslin body, bisque lower arms and legs, painted brown boots, wearing antique man's costume with brown trousers, brown velvet jacket. Condition: generally excellent. Marks: 4 (inside shoulder plate). Comments: Germany, circa 1875. $300/500

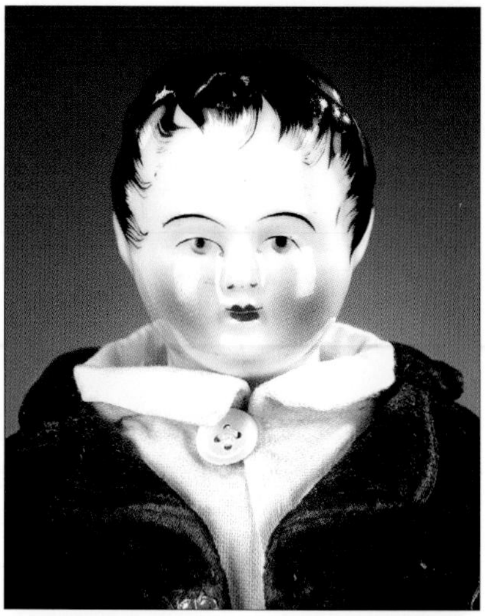

451.

452. *German Paper Mache Doll as Twirling Toy*

9" (23 cm.) Appearing as though standing upon a metal two-part circular stand is a paper mache doll with painted hair and facial features, muslin body, wooden lower limbs with painted high boots, wearing original blue muslin and lace suit with bells. Actually the doll is suspended from a wire rod that attaches to the base and causes the doll to appear to "dance" about when the base is twirled. Excellent condition, nose tip rubbed, toy operates well. Circa 1865. $300/500

452.

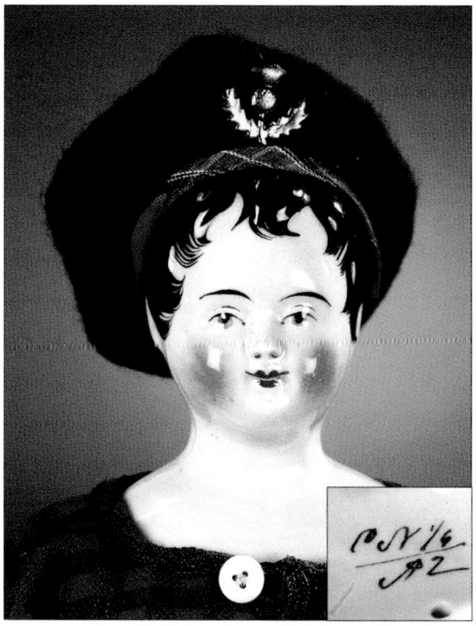

453. *German Pink-tinted Porcelain Boy with Well-Sculpted Hair*

13" (33 cm.) Pink tinted porcelain shoulder head with black sculpted hair in exaggerated tousled fashion, curls onto the face, painted facial features with hint of smile, old muslin body with paper mache lower arms, painted muslin lower legs with painted shoes. Condition: generally excellent. Marks: CN 1/6 A2 (inside shoulder plate, inscribed script). Comments: circa 1850, the rosy cheeked boy was written about by Estrid Faurholt in her *Book of Dolls and Dollhouses*, "This boy was a nice surpise. Early one morning the postman rang and brought this doll as a present from an unknown person who had heard about [my] 'preoccupation'". The doll is wearing its original costume as presented to Mrs. Faurholt and later acquired by Legoland Museum. $800/1100

454. *German Paper Mache Oracle Doll with Original Fortunes and Stand*

8.5" (22 cm.) Paper mache shoulder head portraying woman with black sculpted hair waved over the ears into chignon at back of head, painted facial features, block torso that attached to dowel of original wooden stand, kid arms, original black silk tunic over folded paper "skirt"; each paper in the skirt is actually a "fortune" or oracle for the person selecting it. The fortunes are all German language, indicating its creation for that market. Condition: very good, fine unrestored condition although a tad dusty. Comments: Germany, circa 1845. $600/900

456. *American Mechanical Toy "The Hero of the Cakewalk" by J.M. Cromwell*

9.5" (24 cm.) A paper mache black man with painted facial features, sculpted yellow and red cap, wooden loosely-jointed limbs, painted brown boots, and in original costume is suspended upon a stage with nicely carved background and canopy with fabric curtain which hides the mechanism. When wound, the doll dances about. Condition: very good, some dust to original costume, mechanism functions well. Comments: J.M. Cromwell, circa 1879, the toy was advertised as "The Hero of the Cakewalk", described as a "stylish gentleman of color" who dances in a manner that proves him to be "a master of the Terpsichorean art". The original price was $1.50. $2000/2500

457. *Rare Early German Tilting Doll*

5" (13 cm.) One piece heavy paper mache figure of bonneted woman clasping her taufling baby, the woman's lower body actually ball-shaped to allow it to tilt or rock back and forth while never tipping over. The woman has modeled ruffled Charlotte bonnet over sculpted hair, painted facial features, modeled shawl and the baby has a very expressive painted face. Condition: good, unrestored albeit original paint is faded yet age-darkened. Comments: Germany, circa 1850, a wonderful early toy with silk skirt hiding the rolly-base, and its original wooden tray. The toy was featured on p. 32 of Faurholt's *Book of Dolls and Dollhouses*. $600/900

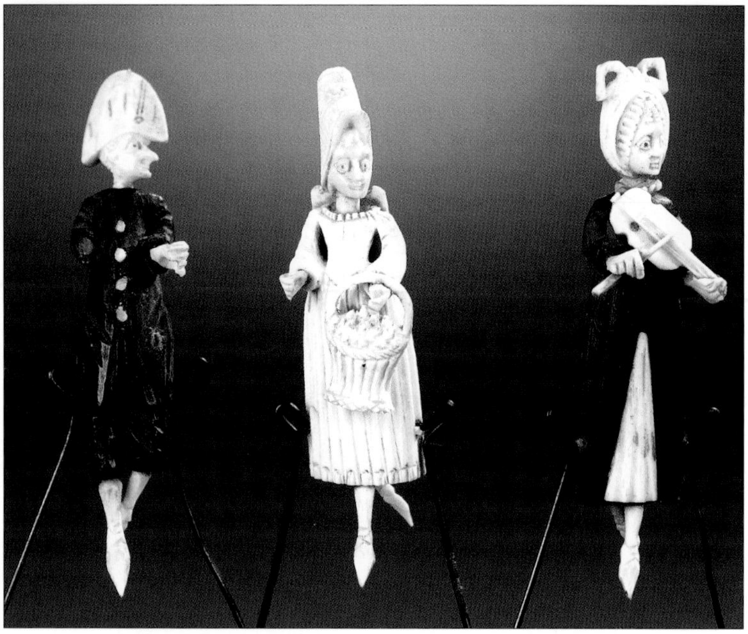

458 detail.

458. *Very Rare Trio of Carved Wood & Bone Balancing Dolls, Possibly 18th Century*

3.5" (9 cm.) 3.5" figures, 5" including weights. Each is intricately carved of fine wood and/or bone with rich detail of facial features, costumes, and accessories that enhance the activity they represent, each with one foot poised for balancing, and each with lead counterweights for balancing. Included are the flower seller with basket of flowers in hand and another basket at her back, the female violinist with elaborate coiffe and violin, and the Marquis with elaborate hat. Condition: two women excellent, man missing right hand. Comments: probably French, 18th century. $1200/1800

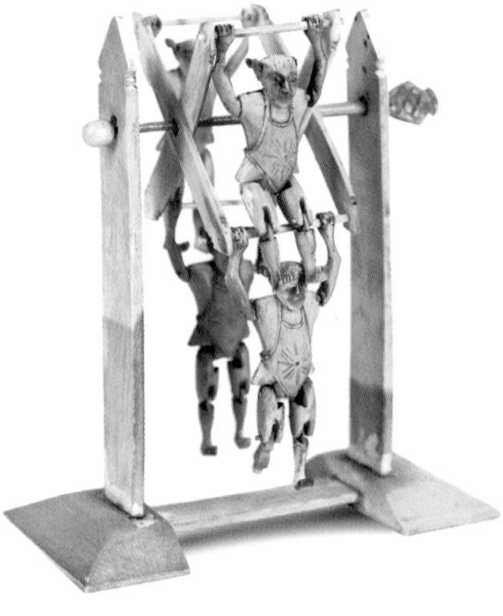

459. *Chinese Early Carved Bone Four-Figure Acrobat Team*

4" (10 cm.) Very delicate carved bone toy represents four tumbling Chinese acrobats, each balanced on an interconnected trapeze with four rods. Each figure has well defined carving of facial features, hair, and costume, with swivel-jointed arms and dowel-jointing at hips and knees. When the wheel is turned they tumble in an infinite number of acrobatic acts. Excellent condition, one foot tip missing. A rare and superb early toy. Chinese, early 19th century. $800/1200

460.

460. *Two Chinese Carved Bone Miniature Tumbling Acrobat Toys*

4" (10 cm.) Each is of carved bone with well defined features and costumes, swivel-jointed at shoulders and dowel-jointed at shoulders and knees. Included is a single figure with exceptional carving, and a double-figure toy. Condition: single figure toy is excellent, double figure toy has missing one balance bar missing and another split. Chinese, mid-19th century. $800/1200

461. *Early Chinese Carved Bone Tumbling Acrobat Toy*

4.5" (11 cm.) An exquisitely carved acrobatic platform supports two interconnected tumbling bars, each with an elaborately carved bone Chinese acrobat, each having rich carving of facial features, costume and shoes, swivel-jointing at shoulders, dowel-jointing at hips and knees. When the balancing rods are turned the acrobats perform in a series in infinite movements. Excellent condition. The detail of platform carving includes the base and exterior sides of support beams. Chinese, mid-19th century. $800/1200

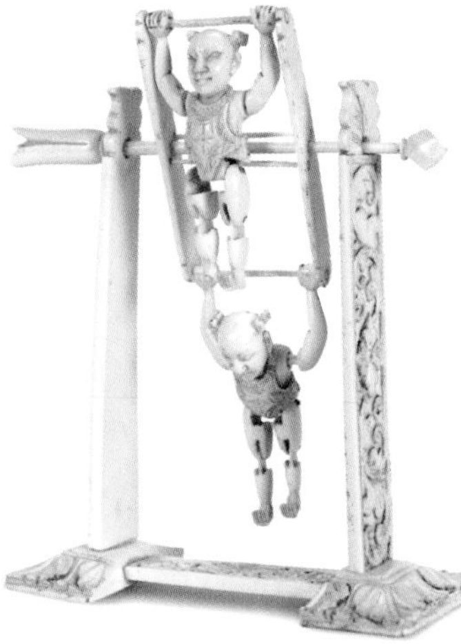

461.

462. *Fine Early Music Box in the Shape of Leather Bookcase*

9.5" (24 cm.) A wooden framed bookcase with gold-tooled leather finish has a beveled glass door that hinges open to a faux-book lined interior. The shelves of books are simply a facade, two forming the front of a drawer, and the top disguising the musical mechanism (1" cylinder,

18 teeth) which is hidden behind, and which plays when the key is wound at the backside and the cabinet door opened. Condition: generally excellent, music functions albeit a bit slowly. Marks: Reuge St. Croix Switzerland (music box). Comments: circa 1890, a luxury "surprise" music box. $700/900

463. *Rare Early Wax :Lady Doll with Sculpted Hair and Cobalt Eyes in Original Costume*

15" (38 cm.) Shoulder head of amber tinted very thick wax over fine layer of paper mache, brown sculpted hair with curls tucked behind the ears, and ringlet curls at the back of the head, cobalt blue glass inset eyes, painted facial features, original commercial muslin body with original wooden lower limbs, painted black flat shoes with red ankle ties and buttons. Condition: generally excellent, some paint wear on wooden limbs. Comments: maker unknown, the style of hair, cobalt eyes, and thick wax along with superb original (albeit frail) gown with pearl appliques and original undergarments suggests an early German model of the 1860 era. These examples are extremely rare to find. The doll was from the original collection of Estrid Faurholt, later acquired by Legoland Museum. $1200/1800

463, 465.

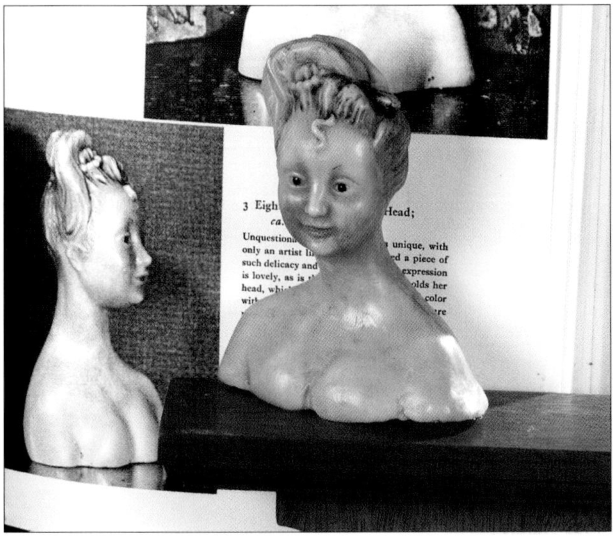

465 detail.

465. *Early Hand-Pressed Wax Doll Bust with Superb Coiffure and Enamel Eyes*

5" (13 cm.) Thick amber-tinted beeswax shoulder head of adult woman with slender oval face turned slightly to the side, elongated throat and well-defined throat hollow and bosom, has sculpted hair in very ornate upswept fashion decorated by a sculpted ornament and beads, one curl onto the mid-forehead, with tiny black enamel eyes in modeled eye sockets, closed mouth, one ear sculpted and the other covered by hair. Condition: generally excellent. Comments: the mystery lady is likely French, and although early a precise dating is difficult. Estrid Faurholt in her *Book of Dolls and Dollhouses* notes that the 18th century is a certainty, adding "unquestionably this wax head is unique with only an artist likely to have created a piece of such delicacy and beauty". $800/1000

467 detail.

466, 467, 468.

466. *Pair of Fine Early Silhouettes in Original Frames*

5.5" (14 cm.) A gentleman and lady in profile facing poses are well detailed with definition of hair and costume, each in its original burled walnut frame with inlay. Each is signed and dated 1823. Very good condition, some light spotting on background paper. $500/800

467. *Early Walnut Miniature Desk with Bone Inlay*

8.5" (22 cm.) An early slant front desk of fine polished walnut with carved edging around the drop front and two lower drawers features two pull-out drawer supports, large wooden knobs, bone inlay keyhole, and a fitted desk interior with pencil drawer, center cabinet with door and four detailed niches. The workmanship is simple, yet most appealing, and the finish carries a fine warm patina. Late 18th century. $800/1100

469 detail.

468. *Early Wax Fashion Lady in Original Elaborate Costume*

15" (38 cm.) Amber tinted wax shoulder head of adult lady with head posed to the side, angular slender features and throat, jointed wax slender arms with wax hands posed for holding objects, linen wrapped armature body with wire frame for posing. The lady wears a very elaborate wig, and a stitched-on gown of brown silk taffeta with superb appliqued decorations, matching bonnet, fan, bouquet, tulle handkerchief and silk slippers. Condition: very good, wax excellent except right arm broken below elbow (held by costume), some costume fraility albeit all original. Comments: probably French, late 18th century, a very rare find in remarkable state of preservation for its age and style. $1200/1800

469.

469. *Danish Porcelain Doll by Royal Copenhagen with Brown Sculpted Hair in Topknot*

17" (43 cm.) 17"h. overall. 4" head. Porcelain shoulder head portraying adult lady with oval face and elongated throat, slightly modeled bosom, brown sculpted hair with long loop curls in front of each ear, and a coiled topknot at the crest, with tendrils of curls onto the nape, old muslin body with blue leather lower arms, wearing antique patterned homespun gown, undergarments, stitched on slippers. Condition: generally excellent. Marks: (three lines with dot, inside shoulderplate). Comments: Royal Copenhagen, circa 1840, the doll head was shown in Faurholt's *Book of Dolls and Dollhouses* and she noted "it might very well have been the first [model] ever made in the factory". $2500/3500

470. *Three Early German Porcelain Doll Heads*

3.5" (9 cm.) 3.5" heads, 8" partial doll. Each of porcelain with sculpted hair in various styles and painted facial features, including blonde curly haired head with flanged neck, black short hair with forehead stippling and flanged neck, and a partial taufling baby with swivel head, matching porcelain breast plate, lower midriff and lower arms, muslin midriff and upper arms. Condition: blonde head reglued, taufling has neck chips at back upper torso. Comments: Germany, circa 1860, rare models in various style. $400/600

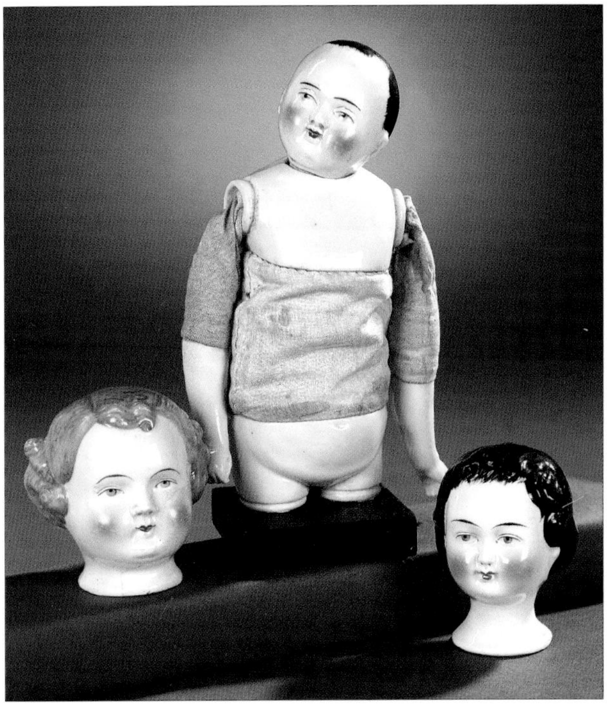

470.

471. *German Bisque Flirty-Eyed Toddler by Kestner*

18" (46 cm.) Bisque socket head, brown glass side-glancing "flirty" eyes, open mouth, two upper teeth, brunette mohair wig, composition ball-jointed toddler body, antique costume including a great pair of shoes. Condition: generally excellent. Marks: made in Germany 257 JDK. Comments: Kestner, circa 1915. $500/600

472. *Early German Paper Mache "Elephant in the Box" Toy*

7" (18 cm.) A narrow wooden box with lithographed paper cover has a surprise when the box lid is opened: a paper mache elephant with painted features, long accordian-trunk and original muslin costume with bowtie pops up in traditional "jack in the box" style. Excellent condition except lacking paper on upper wooden lid. Germany, circa 1880. $300/500

473. *German Wooden Animal Menagerie Wagon with Animals*

12" (30 cm.) A wooden cage cart with metal spoked wheels has original green paint and red paper lithographed roof, has hinged front door which, when opened, releases a fierce glass eyed lion that is posed on a spring-driven platform. Side doors also open, and included inside are five different composition animals marked "Lineol" (added later). Condition: generally excellent, one tin wheel missing. Comments: Germany, circa 1900. $400/600

474. *German Bisque Toddler by K*R*

10" (25 cm.) Bisque socket head, brown glass sleep eyes, open mouth, two teeth, original brunette mohair bobbed wig, original five piece composition toddler body with chubby torso, antique dress, knit panties, stockings, good old leather shoes. Condition: generally excellent, body especially nice except one thumb missing. Marks: K*R Simon & Halbig 126 Germany 2/0. Comments: Kammer and Reinhardt, circa 1920, a dear toddler with original wig and rare body. $500/700

473, 474.

475. German Tin Penny Toy "Girl Feeding Rooster" by Meier

3.5" (9 cm.) Standing upon a spoked-wheel embossed platform with original green paint is a girl with red head scarf, her apron holding bird feed, facing a colorful rooster. Marked Ges Gesch with dog and cart symbol. Meier, circa 1910. Very good condition, some light paint wear. $300/400

476. German Tin Mechanical Penny Toy, "Boy on Cart" by Meier

3" (8 cm.) A four-wheeled pale green platform with darker green seat holds a seated boy in lithographed sailor suit, holding steering rod. Movement of wheels causes the boy to tilt forward and back. Marked Germany. An identical model has been found with the Meier's insignia. Excellent condition. Germany, circa 1910. $400/500

477. German Tin Mechanical Penny Toy "The Bicycle Carousel" by Meier

3" (8 cm.) Arranged upon a fluted tin platform with red roof are six tin cyclists on two-wheel cycles. When the lever is push-pulled, the riders briskly move around the platform in unison. Bike wheel marked "Ges Gesch", and Meier dog and cart insignia on the base. Germany, circa 1915. $500/700

478. German Tin Penny Toy Bank as a Gingerbread House

3" (8 cm.) An embossed lithographed tin house-shaped box has designs of Hansel and Gretel with the wicked Witch. The slanted roof top has a slot for coins and key lock mechanism (no key). Excellent condition. Circa 1910. $300/400

479. German Tin Mechanical Penny Toy, "The Feeding Ducks" by Meier

2.5" (6 cm.) A yellow lithographed embossed duck house rests upon a red platform, and contains two ducks which bob their heads up and down as though feeding when the handle at the side is turned. Very good condition, feeding tray missing. Signed Ges Gesch and having Meier dog and cart symbol. Germany, circa 1910. $300/400

480. German Tin Mechanical Penny Toy "Bobbing Goose on Platform"

4" (10 cm.) Standing upon a wheeled green tin platform is a grey goose with orange feet and beak, the head and long neck loosely jointed to the body. When the goose is pulled along, its head bobs up and down. Excellent condition. Germany, circa 1910. $300/400

481, 482, 483.

flywheel movement that causes the cars to revolve in a realistic manner. Condition: very good, minor paint wear on platform and few people, mechanism functions well. Marks: made in Germany (and impressed symbol on intertwined letters inside six-sided box). Comments: Germany, circa 1900. $500/900

484. *German Tin Mechanical Airship Ferris Wheel*

10" (25 cm.) Heavy tin toy presents an unusual ferris wheel, having airships as the passenger cars, each oval car surmounted by an oval balloon, the platform decorated with four colorful flags, and the mechanism operated by a manual crank that allows the cars not only to revolve but to tip and turn within their own axis. Condition: good to very good, the base rim and one car are repainted red, there is one passenger (3 appear to be missing), mechanism functions well. Comments: Germany, circa 1895. $600/900

481. *German Porcelain Boy with Sculpted Short Black Hair*

13" (33 cm.) Porcelain shoulder head with short black sculpted hair in well-detailed stippled curls around the face, painted facial features, muslin body, porcelain limbs. Condition: generally excellent, hairline on one leg. Marks: E1 5t (script on inside back shoulder plate). Comments: Germany, circa 1870, excellent detail of hair painting, with fine antique boy's costume. $400/600

482. *German Porcelain Boy with Sculpted Short Black Curly Hair*

14" (36 cm.) Porcelain shoulder head, black short curly hair with unusual detail of sculpting and stippled curls around the forehead and nape of neck, painted facial features, sculpted ears, muslin stitch-jointed body, porcelain lower arms. Condition: generally excellent. Marks: 436.3 (ink script inside shoulder plate). Comments: Germany, circa 1865, excellent detail of hair, fine antique blue woolen suit, leather shoes. $400/600

483. *German Tin Mechanical Ferris Wheel*

13" (33 cm.) Tinplate ferris wheel with painted cream/green structure, and six lithographed tin cars and passengers with colorful costumes, has

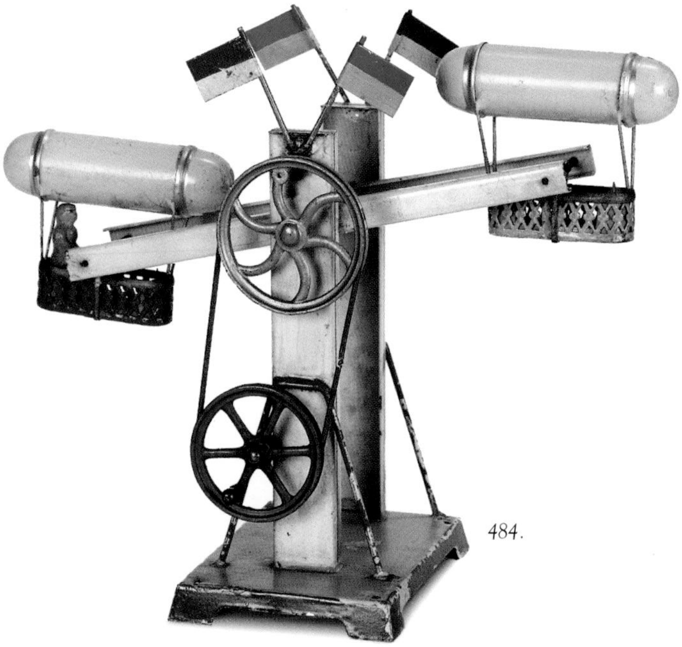

484.

485.

486.

485. *French Miniature Circus with Lead Figures and Original Stage*

22" (56 cm.) 22"l x 10"d x 6"h. A wooden framed box with removable lid and hinged front serves as the display for a miniature circus with a myriad of little lead figures comprising performers, animals, public, police, the orchestra, and accessoreis including flags, oil lamps, plants, and even a painted canopy and circus ring. There are 24 people, five animals including a monkey balanced on a pig, a performing horse, and an elephant that balances the acrobat's ladder. Condition: generally excellent, some wear to outer lid of box. Marks: CBG Paris (paper label). Comments: Cuperly, Blondel and Gerbeau, circa 1890, a rare and visually stunning presentation set. $900/1300

486. *German Tin Lithographed Mechanical Miniature Handcar*

3.5" (9 cm.) A tin lithographed wind-up toy features a four-wheel car with brightly decorated sides including passenger profiles. Standing on the front and rear bumpers are a pair of dimensionally-figured men with hinged arms, each holding onto the frame of the car. When wound and activated the men busily pump the handcar back and forth which, assumedly, moves the car. Condition: very good, colors fresh and vibrant albeit a bit darkened on window frames, mechanism functions when held in hand, but may be missing a piece of the underside that would cause car to move when placed on the ground. Marks" DRP DRGM Germany. Comments: circa 1915. $300/500

487. *German Pull-toy "Girl on Carousel Horse with Clown" by Zinner and Sohn*

14" (36 cm.) A wooden platform with paper lithographed cover and metal spoked wheels presents a paper mache clown with painted features, clown costume, wooden arms and legs, and a china head doll seated upon a flannel-covered dappled wooden horse and harness and saddle. When the toy is pulled along, the clown moves his arms up and down as though chasing the horse, and the horse rocks back and forth. Very good condition, a bit dusty, and wear to paper. Germany, Zinner and Sohn, circa 1895. $800/1200

488.

489.

490.

488. *Grand Collection of American Wooden/Bisque Schoenhut Figures*

8" (20 cm.) Comprising people, animals and accessories from the fabled American toy, viz. bisque head ringmaster and acrobatt lady, carved head lion tamer, 2 hobos, 2 Chinamen, and 2 clowns; painted eye animals, viz, brown horse with carved mane, bulldog, lion, double-hump camel and ostrich; glass-eye animals, viz, mountain goat, rhinoceros, dappled horse, poodle elephant and pig; and 14 accessories. Fair to very good condition. American, Schoenhut, circa 1910. $2000/2500

489. *American Wooden Pouty Child by Schoenhut*

15" (38 cm.) All wooden doll has pressed/carved socket head, painted facial features, brown eyes, closed mouth, pouty expression, brunette mohair wig, spring-jointed body, nicely costumed. Condition: generally excellent, rub on nose tip. Marks Schoenhut Doll Pat. Jan 17, 1911 USA. Comments: Schoenhut, circa 1912. $800/1200

490. *American Wooden Circus, Reduced Size, in Original Box by Schoenhut*

7" (18 cm.) Contained in their large original box with colorful circus illustration on the lid, including an American flag, are reduced size wooden circus figures by Schoenhut, comprising, ringmaster (missing hat), bareback rider, and three clowns, along with dappled horse, brown horse, two donkeys, leopard, and 10 various accessories. The box is labeled on the lid and or the side "Schoenhut's Humpty Dumpty Circus No 21/33". Contents very good, box very worn. Circa 1925. $800/1200

491. *Early Wooden Bedpost Folk Doll*

10" (25 cm.) Nicely shaped wooden bedpost style doll has defined sculpting of simplistic facial features and ears, suggestion of carved hair, waist, throat. Excellent condition. Mid-19th century. $200/400

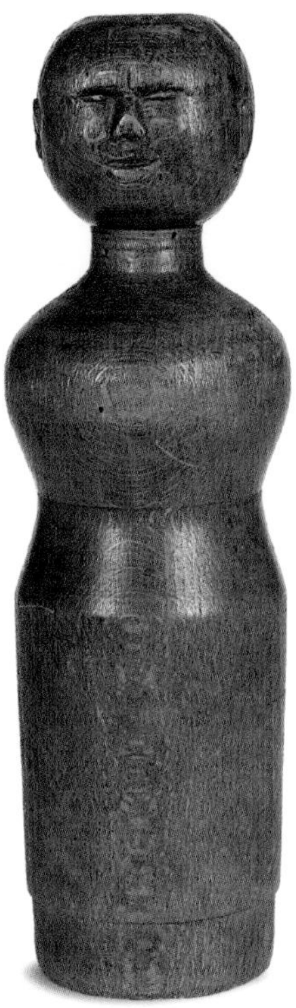

492, 493.

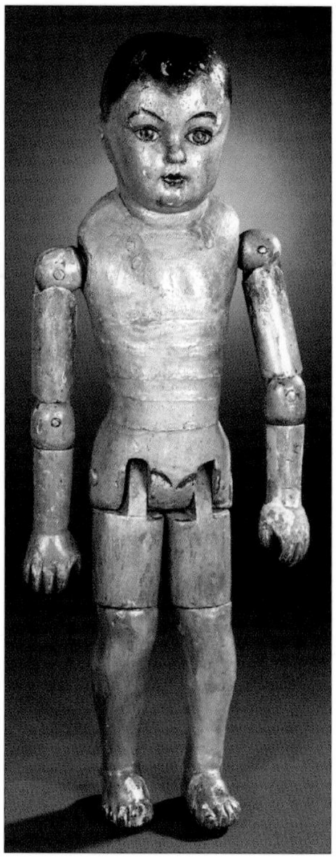

495 detail.

492. *Two German Bisque Dolls in Matching Costumes*

19" (48 cm.) Each has bisque socket head, blue glass eyes, open mouth, blonde human hair, four teeth, composition ball-jointed body. Condition: each has faint hairline not readily visible. Marks: PM 914 (red), S(pb) H 1909 (blue). Comments: Germany, circa 1910, the girls are wearing matching antique knit winter school costumes. $400/500

494, 495.

493. *Rare 19th Century Scandinavia Riding Horse*

25" (64 cm.) 25"l. A heavy wooden riding horse with simplistic carving features a cast iron handle with wooden grip, painted detail's of horse head, carved and fancily painted horse legs and decorations, black leather "saddle". Excellent original condition. Mid -19th century. $400/500

494. *Commercial Wooden Toy Riding Horse*

19" (48 cm.) Flat-dimension wooden horse has dappled grey painted finish, black button eyes, leather harness and a wide "saddle" with red diamond-point trim, heavy cast iron casters at the feet bottoms. The underside is stenciled "2". An appealing folk toy in well-preserved condition. Circa 1900. $300/400

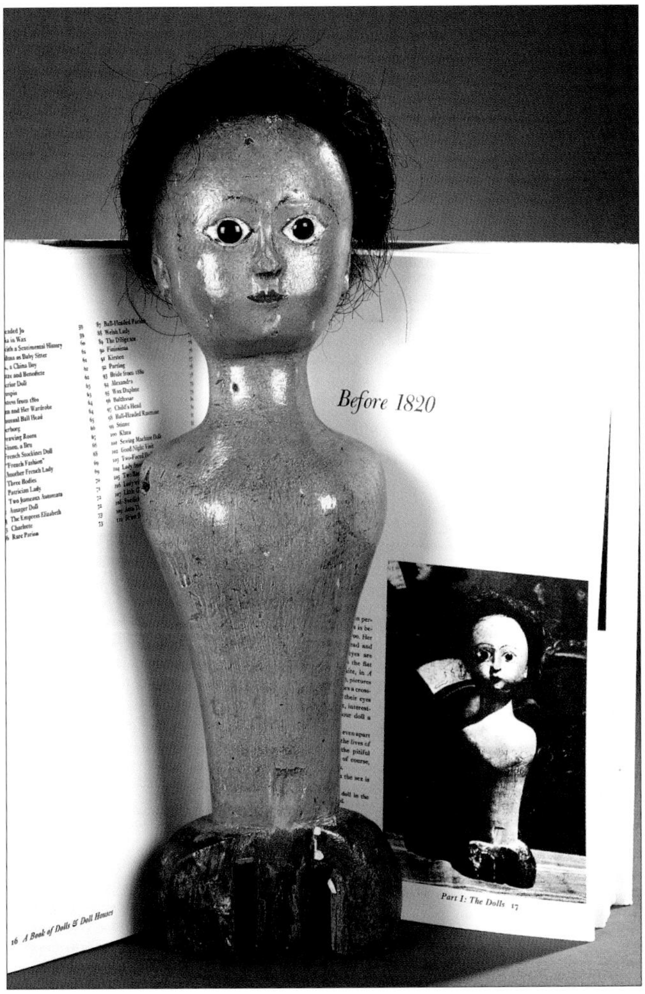

496.

497. *Early Knit Woolen Scandinavian Doll*

13" (33 cm.) A simple yet appealing folk doll having woolen knit features and costume, defined nose, embroidered features, stitched on red woolen tassel cap and "beard", red woolen sweater with defined hands, black trousers, socks, and black shoes. Circa 1900. Excellent condition. $300/400

497.

498. *Collection of Children's Wooden Toys*

11" (28 cm.) All wooden toys in the classical tradition include an 11" ball and cup toy with stenciled colors, 6 tops in beautifully finish maple in various styles, and 2 additional toys in rich colored design. Early 20th century. Excellent condition. $300/500

495. *Early Wooden Hand-Carved Play Doll*

23" (58 cm.) All-wooden doll has one-piece head and torso, painted brown hair and facial features, crudely dowel and pin jointed at shoulders, elbows, hips and knees, extra swivel jointing in lower arms. Condition: well-loved, finish appears original yet varnished, paint flaking and wear on face and arms. Comments: folk art doll, clumsily yet charmingly created with imaginative details, the doll has its original cotton costume. Circa 1890. $400/600

496. *Large Early Wooden "Venerable" Doll Form*

15" (38 cm.) One piece wooden head and torso with shapely waist and bosom, black enamel eyes, carve-defined nose, philtrum and ears, paint-over-gesso complexion and features. Condition: fair/good, as is. Comments: English, late 18th century, from the original collection of Estrid Faurholt who described the fragment doll as "Venerable", the model is notable for its large size, and worthy of restoration. $500/800

498.

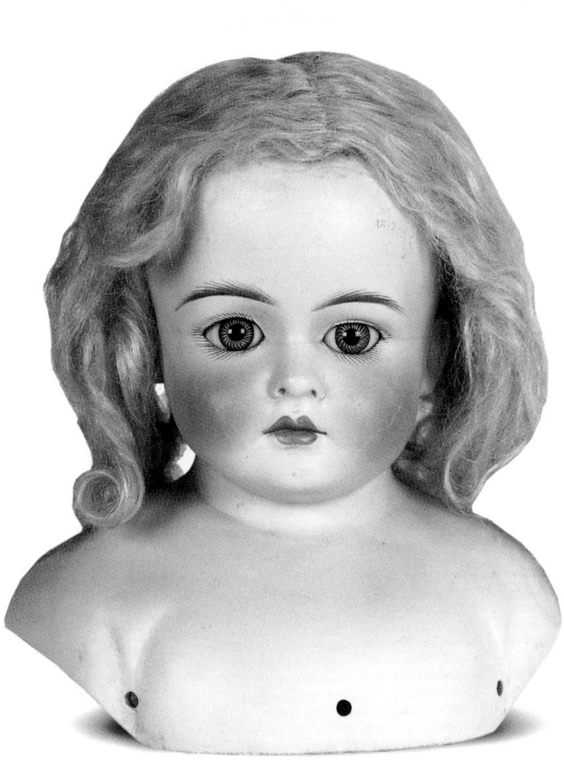

499. *Beautiful Large Bisque Doll Head by Kling*

7" (18 cm.) Bisque shoulder head with solid dome, blue glass eyes, closed mouth, blonde mohair wig. Condition: fine restoration to back shoulderplate. Marks: 167-1. Comments: Kling, circa 1890, an especially beautiful face. $200/300

500. *German Bisque Child by Kling, Model 131 with Painted Eyes*

16" (41 cm.) Bisque shoulder head with blonde sculpted hair in deeply sculpted forehead curls, short curls around the head, painted facial features, blue painted eyes, closed mouth, pouty expression, muslin stitch-jointed body with sewn-on leather boots, antique dress and undergarments. Condition: generally excellent, restoration to right hand. Marks: 131 (bell symbol) K 6. Comments: Kling, circa 1885. $500/700

500, 501.

502.

501. *German Bisque Doll by Kling, Model 131 with Glass Eyes*

17" (43 cm.) Bisque shoulder head with sculpted blonde hair having deep forehead bangs and short curls at back of head, brown glass inset eyes, painted features, closed mouth with downcast expression, muslin stitch-jointed body, bisque lower arms, nicely costumed, rose cotton dress with lace, undergarments, knit stockings, leather shoes. Condition: generally excellent. Marks: 131 (bell symbol) K 6. Comments: Kling, circa 1890, a glass-eyed variation of Doll #500. $500/700

503, 504.

502. *Beautiful German Bisque Doll by Kling in Original Folklore Costume*

17" (43 cm.) Bisque shoulder head with blue glass eyes, closed mouth, rounded nose, blonde mohair wig, kid gusset-jointed body, bisque forearms. Condition: generally excellent, 3 fingertips chipped. Marks: 123 5. Comments: Kling, circa 1890. Value Points: very beautiful model with gentle expression wearing her original Danish folklore costume including woolen costume, embroidered silk ribbons, silver jewelry, metallic trim on sleeves and coiffe, woolen petticoats, undergarments, shoes. $900/1300

503. *German Bisque Doll by Kling, Model 167 with Open Mouth, Glass Eyes and Wig*

16" (41 cm.) Bisque shoulder head, brown glass eyes, painted facial features, open mouth, four teeth, blonde mohair wig, pink kid pin-jointed body, composition lower arms, antique costume. Condition: generally excellent, hands scuffed. Marks: 167 (bell symbol) K 5. Comments: Kling, circa 1890. $400/600

505.

506.

507.

504. *German Bisque Doll by Kling, Model 167 with Closed Mouth, Glass Eyes and Wig*

13" (33 cm.) Bisque shoulder head, brown glass eyes, painted facial features, closed mouth, brunette mohair wig, muslin torso and upper limbs, bisque lower arms and legs, antique undergarments. Condition: generally excellent. Marks: 167-1. Comments: Kling, circa 1890, the bare feet are rare variation. $400/500

505. *German Bisque Doll by Kling, Model 183 with Modeled Hair and Glass Eyes*

16" (41 cm.) Bisque shoulder head with blonde sculpted hair having deeply sculpted bangs and short curls, closed mouth, painted facial features, kid gusset-jointed body, bisque forearms, antique costume. Condition: generally excellent, kid body a bit worn, right thumb tip missing. Marks: 183-6. Comments: Kling, circa 1885. $500/700

506. *German Bisque Doll by Kling, Model 190 with Sculpted Hair and Glass Eyes*

15" (38 cm.) Bisque shoulder head with blonde sculpted hair in wavy curls across the forehead and overall back of head, blue glass eyes, painted features, closed mouth, muslin body, bisque lower arms, beautiful antique dress of white pique with soutache embroidery. Condition: generally excellent. Marks: 190 4. Comments: Kling, circa 1880. $400/600

507. *German Bisque Doll by Kling, Model 195, with Sculpted Hair and Painted Eyes*

16" (41 cm.) Bisque shoulder head with deeply sculpted blonde hair waved away from face, held by black hair band, curls at the back of the head, muslin stitch-jointed body, bisque lower arms, antique cotton gown and undergarments, leather shoes. Condition: generally excellent. Marks: 195-3. Comments: Kling, circa 1880. $400/500

508.

509.

508. *German Bisque Toddler, 1070, by Konig and Warnecke*

22" (56 cm.) Bisque socket head, blue glass sleep eyes, painted facial features, open mouth, two porcelain teeth, brunette mohair wig, composition ball-jointed toddler body, great antique costume with net schoolbag. Condition: generally excellent. Marks: K&W 1070 10. Comments: Konig and Warnecke, circa 1912, expressive features and fine luminous bisque. $700/900

509. *German Bisque Character, 122, by Simon and Halbig with Rare Body*

16" (41 cm.) Bisque socket head, blue glass sleep eyes, painted facial features, open mouth, two porcelain upper teeth, brunette human hair, composition toddler body with side-hip jointed walking style legs (causing head to turn side to side), toddler arms with unusual elbow jointing, cotton suit. Condition: generally excellent. Marks: P Simon & Halbig 122P 36 Germany. Comments: Simon and Halbig, circa 1912, unusual letter P with mystery significance, rare body style, included is old golden miniature teddy bear. $800/1100

510. *Rare Nuremburg Tin Mechanical Peacock "Pao-Pao" by Hans Eberl*

9.5" (24 cm.) Painted tin peacock with deeply embossed feather design on long tail feathers, has coilspring mechanical movement with attached bellows that causes the peacock to strut proudly along, turning head side to side, while bellows creates a peacock sound. Excellent condition of movement, bellows needs restoration, painting is original and beautifully preserved. Marked "Ebo Pao-Pao, Made in Germany DRGM" with clown in circle symbol. Hans Eberl, Nuremburg, circa 1910. $700/900

511. *Early Nuremburg Tin Mechanical Duck Attributed to Gunthermann*

6.5" (17 cm.) Painted tin duck with dark brown head and ochre shaded wings with outlined details, painted eyes and beak, with internal voice bellows and three wheel base. When wound, the duck flaps its wings and moves forward, while the bellows (not working) causes it to quack. Very good condition, mechanism functions, some repair at inner edges of wings. Attributed to Gunthermann, Nuremburg, Germany, circa 1890. $500/800

512. *German Tin Mechanical Goose*

5.5" (14 cm.) Painted tin goose in original soft shades of creamy ochre with blue painted under-neck and face, painted eyes, yellow beak, with separate wings, and two large spoked wheels and a tiny balance wheel at the back. When wound, the goose moves along while his wings briskly flap up and down. Marked "Made in Germany". Circa 1900. Excellent condition, one paint flake on wing, movement functions well. $600/800

510.

511.

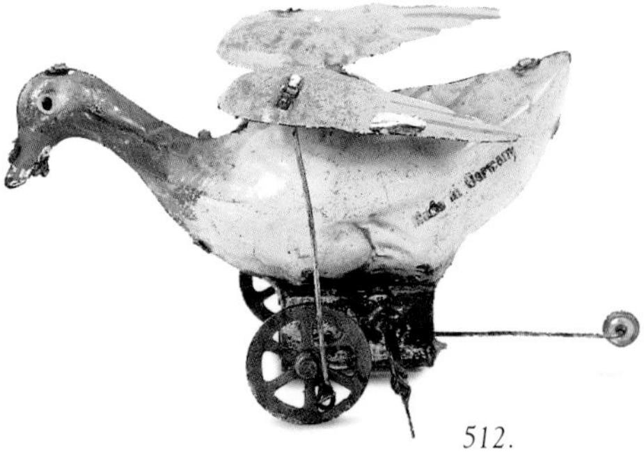

512.

513.

513. *German Bisque Toddler with Toy Lamb*

15" (38 cm.) Bisque socket head, blue glass sleep eyes, open mouth, two upper teeth, brunette human hair bobbed wig, composition toddler body, nicely costumed. Condition: generally excellent. Marks: 914 6. Comments: circa 1915, included with the toddler is a toy paper mache lamb. $400/500

514.

514. *German Bisque Character by K*R with Signed Wig*

16" (41 cm.) Bisque socket head, blue glass sleep eyes, painted facial features, open mouth, two teeth, blonde mohair wig, composition baby body, antique baby dress. Condition: generally excellent, wig pulls under wig at back of head. Marks: K*R 22 Germany 7. Comments: Kammer and Reinhardt, circa 1920, the doll has wonderful antique wig in like-new condition with original label "Trademark GeteFrisue Schutzmarke Germany 30". $400/500

515. *Early Tin Mechanical Toy Bird*

6" (15 cm.) Pressed tin bird with painted dark green feathers and head, black beak, creamy underbelly, embossed feather design, is attached to wheeled base with mechanism. When wound, the bird moves along and feathers flap up and down. Excellent condition, paint beautifully preserved with minor darkening where attached to mechanism. Circa 1895. $500/700

516. *Early Painted Tin Mechanical Toy "Woman Chasing Ducks"*

11" (28 cm.) Pressed tin toy with hand-painted finish features a woman with brown painted topknot hair, painted facial features, painted costume with green skirt and scarf and brown apron, standing behind a row of mother duck and baby duck, each with painted feathers and eyes. When wound, the parade briskly moves along on its wheeled base, and the woman moves her arms up and down as though chasing the ducks away from her back door. Excellent condition, few paint flakes, object missing from woman's right hand and original slit in right side of baby duck suggests possibly an original flap (but not on left side). Circa 1895. $800/1100

515.

516.

517.

518.

519.

520.

517. *Pair, Swiss Dolls with Ball-Bearing Bodies by Bucherer*

8" (20 cm.) Depicting an adult man and woman each with composition head, painted hair and features, all metal body with ball-bearing jointing allowing infinite articulation, composition hands and feet with painted shoes, original costumes. Condition: generally excellent. Comments: Bucherer, the Swiss watchmaker created a series of dolls with these unique bodies, circa 1920. $300/500

518. *Two Stereopticans with Collection of Early Photographic Views*

12" (30 cm.) Including an all wood model along with a wooden and silver-plated model from Underwood & Underwood, dated 1910, and a large number of early optican views, including some unusual interior home views, and other historic views of Danish localities. Very good to excellent condition. $300/400

519. *German Tin Mechanical "The Performing Sea Lion" by Lehmann*

7" (18 cm.) 7"l. A lithographed tin sea lion in shades of grey, black and cream has painted eyes, and red collar, hinged flippers and tail, a large wheel at his under belly and two tiny wheels under the tail. When wound, he propels along as though swimming, his flippers move in a complicated manner and his tail swings. Condition: excellent, original finish well preserved, mechanism functions well, key missing. Marks: (early EPL mark and various patent notes stamped on underside of tail). Comments: Ernst Paul Lehmann, circa 1900, the toy was marketed as "The Performing Sea Lion" and was inspired by Lehmann's visit to San Francisco's Cliff House where he watched the seals sunning themselves on the rocks, according to Cieslik's book, Lehmann Toys. $700/900

520. *Early Nuremburg Mechanical Toy "Dogs Fighting for the Bone"*

11" (28 cm.) 11"l. excluding tail. Two pressed tin dachshunds with hand-painted finish in shades of brown and black with painted lighter underbelly, and defined eyes and collars, have tiny coil-spring tails, and are attached at the nose with a bone between them. The brown dog is mounted on a two wheel base with mechanism attached, and the black dog has narrow balance wheel. When activated, the dogs move forward and backward, side to side, as though fighting over the bone, while the spring tails wag vigorously. Excellent condition, original paint is wonderfully preserved with few small flakes, mechanism functions well. Germany, Nuremburg, circa 1890. $1100/1500

521. *Four Swiss Comic Character Dolls by Bucherer*

8" (20 cm.) 8" Maggie. Each of four characters has composition head with highly characterized features, metal ball-bearing body, composition hands and feet, and wears original flannel costume. Condition: good to excellent, Peter's nose is rubbed, some costume dust. Comments: Bucherer, the Swiss clockmaker created a series of figures, circa 1920's, with unique metal ball-bearing bodies. Included here is Maggie, Popeye's Bluto and two characters from a rare Danish cartoon, Peter and Ping, popular from 1922-1949. $600/900

521.

522. *German Bisque Character "Baby Stuart" by Gebruder Heubach*

10" (25 cm.) Bisque shoulder head with sculpted baby bonnet decorated with roses and trailing vines, painted facial features, pouty expression, muslin body with bisque lower arms and legs, bare bisque feet, nicely costumed. Condition: generally excellent. Marks: Heubach (in square) 8226 Germany. Comments: Gebruder Heubach, circa 1915, the rarer shoulder head model with rare bisque feet. $300/500

523. *Two German Bisque Character Babies by Heubach*

9.5" (24 cm.) 9.5" largest. Each has bisque socket head with painted hair, painted facial features, one with wide beaming smile, and the other with pouty lips, each with closed mouth, intaglio eyes, composition baby body, nicely costumed in antique baby dresses and blankets and pillow. Condition: generally excellent. Marks: Heubach (sunburst mark). Comments: Gebruder Heubach, circa 1912. $500/700

524. *Nuremburg Painted Tin Mechanical Toy "Cat with Mouse in Cage"*

11" (28 cm.) Pressed tin toy with hand-painted details, richly embossed details of cat's body including fur, ears and tail, with original brown/yellow shaded finish portrays a cat in pouncing position watching a mouse that has been captured in a trip. The cat rests upon a wheeled base with painted green/cream spoked wheels, matching the cage. When wound, the toy propels forward and about, while the mouse simultaneously races around the cage as though trying to escape. Condition: original painted finish albeit quite worn, mechanism functions well. Germany, circa 1890. $500/800

524.

525, 526.

527.

525. French Bisque Character Boy by SFBJ

18" (46 cm.) Solid domed bisque socket head, narrow blue glass eyes, closed mouth with smiling expression, flocked hair, French composition fully-jointed body. Condition: generally excellent. Marks: SFBJ 235 Paris 6. Comments: SFBJ, circa 1912, the boy wears his original white wool sailor suit, socks and shoes. $800/1200

526. French Mechanical Toy, Boy Pulling Girl in Cart, by Roullet et Decamps

13" (33 cm.) 13"l. A bisque headed boy (marked 550 GH) with carton torso containing clockwork mechanism has painted facial features, composition lower limbs, and is pulling a two-wheeled wooden cart upon which a small bisque-headed doll (marked G.K. 44-17) is seated. When wound, the boy briskly moves legs forward and backward, and "pulls" the cart along. Condition: very good, costumes not original albeit old, mechanism functions well. Comments: Roullet et Decamps, circa 1910. $1100/1500

527. German Handwind Mechanical Scene "The Dance Party"

9.5" (24 cm.) 11" x 8" base, 9.5" larger doll. Posed upon a wooden stage with fabric covering to suggest a carpet are three bisque-head dolls, each with glass eyes and mohair wig, wooden limbs. When handwound at the side, the two larger dolls play the violins they hold, while the smaller doll twirls around and around as though dancing, while music plays. Condition: bisque heads excellent, mechanism functions well, costumes not original and very dusty. Comments: in the manner of Zinner and Sohn, circa 1895. $800/1100

528.

528. German Bisque Doll as Musical Marotte

15" (38 cm.) A bisque shoulder head with blue glass eyes and blonde mohair wig is attached to a ball-shaped form that contains a musical box and a maple wood handle. The form is costumed in a festive magenta silk with fringe, and when the handle is turned the doll twirls about and music plays. Excellent condition, costume partially original. Circa 1900. $400/500

529. German Novelty Toy with Unusual Mechanical Doll

6" (15 cm.) 6" seated. A bisque-headed doll with blue glass eyes, open mouth, and blonde mohair wig is attached to unusual body, posed seated, with composition arms, and legs bent at knees, a simple mechanical device hidden under the costume that, when wound, causes the doll to lean forward and backward, while rolling forward and sideways as though scooting along in playful movement. Condition: generally excellent, mechanism functions well. Comments: Germany, head by Simon and Halbig, circa 1900. $400/600

530. German Bisque Doll with Mechanical Walking Movement

8" (20 cm.) Bisque head doll with blue glass eyes, open mouth, brunette wig, is attached to carton torso with cone-shaped skirt that contains a simple winding mechanical movement that causes the doll to walk, turn and repeat the movement in a simple manner. There are three wheels at the base, and the movement is covered by the doll's costume. Condition: mechanism functions well although tiny back wheel needs repair. Comments: Germany, circa 1915. $300/400

531. Collection, Three Party Musical Marottes with Bisque Heads

14" (36 cm.) 14" tallest. Each has bisque shoulder head with glass inset eyes, and is attached to ball-shaped torso form with long stick handle. When the stick is twirled the dolls revolve about in a festive manner and music plays. Condition: very good, played with and general dustiness, music and twirling function well. Comments: Germany, circa 1900. $500/800

532. Three German Tin Lithographed Miniature Carriages

4" (10 cm.) Each is of tin with lithographed design, various styles of doll strollers and carriages in miniature form, including unusual blue carriage with cover having lithographed image of black baby in bunting holding a bottle, and another model with scenes on the side of children playing with dolls. Very good/excellent condition. Germany, circa 1920. $200/300

533, 534, 535.

536.

533. Petite German Black Haired Porcelain Lady with Ornate Hair

10" (25 cm.) Porcelain shoulder head with black sculpted hair arranged with chignon and long curls onto the shoulders, muslin body, leather hands, wearing nice antique costume. Condition: generally excellent. Comments: Germany, circa 1885. $300/400

534. Doll's Country-Style Wooden Secretary Desk with Roll-Front

18" (46 cm.) Wooden secretary desk with roll-front desk lid, has three bottom drawers, interior drawers and niche, and a fancy top with mirrored niche, and two closed door cupboards, with pediment crest, fancy candelabra included. Excellent condition, albeit of a simple rustic style construction. Circa 1890. $300/400

535. Petite German Black Haired Porcelain Doll

10" (25 cm.) Porcelain shoulder head with black sculpted short curly hair, painted facial features, muslin body, porcelain limbs. Condition: generally excellent, left arm and right leg not original. Comments: Germany, circa 1880, the petite model has well sculpted hair and antique gown. $300/400

536. English Transfer Ware Doll's Dinner Service

3" (8 cm.) 3" tureen. Of white softpaste porcelain with blue transfer designs in floral pattern, the service comprises, two lidded tureens with underliners (one with ladle), 3 rectangular platters, 1 oval serving bowl, 5 small plates, 5 large plates, 2 bowls, 6 dessert plates, 1 gravy dish, 1 covered dish, 1 spare cover, and 1 footed vase (hairline). The set is marked Ashworth with a crown (incised). Excellent condition except as noted. English, circa 1880. $300/500

537. *Lovely German Porcelain Lady with Pink Tinted Compelxion*

14" (36 cm.) Pink tinted porcelain shoulder head with elongated throat, oval face, black sculpted hair in deep waves away from face into rolled chignon at back of head, painted facial features, muslin stitch-jointed body, leather arms. Condition: small piece broken off back right corner of shoulderplate by sew hole, otherwise excellent. Comments: Germany, circa 1860, the doll has a lovely early costume, luminous porcelain and expression. $400/500

538.

539, 540.

538. *Three Early Small Scrap Albums*

7" (18 cm.) 7" x 5" red album. The three autograph-sized albums each have gilt fancy lettering on the cover "Album", and inside are beautiful early engravings and lithographs in unusual petite sizes including many of children at play. Circa 1880. $300/400

539. *Slender German Porcelain Lady with Sculpted Black Fancy Hair*

18" (46 cm.) Porcelain shoulder head with black sculpted hair in elaborate arranged curls with head band at the crown, partially sculpted ears, painted facial features, kid body. Condition: generally excellent. Comments: Germany, circa 1875, the lady wears a beautiful early gown that complements perfectly her eyes. $500/700

540. *Elegant German Porcelain Lady with Unusual Coiffure*

22" (56 cm.) Porcelain shoulder head of adult lady with elongated face and throat, black sculpted hair in elaborate fashion waved from forehead into large crown of curls that are formally arranged at the back of head and tumble into a large tendril at the neck, with unusual wide part at the crest that is decorated by a black hair ornament, painted facial features, large blue eyes, sculpted pierced ears, kid fashion body with gusset jointing, separated fingers. Condition: generally excellent, few rubs on hair at back of head. Comments: Germany, circa 1870, the elegant lady wears a lovely early gown, undergarments, leather boots. $600/800

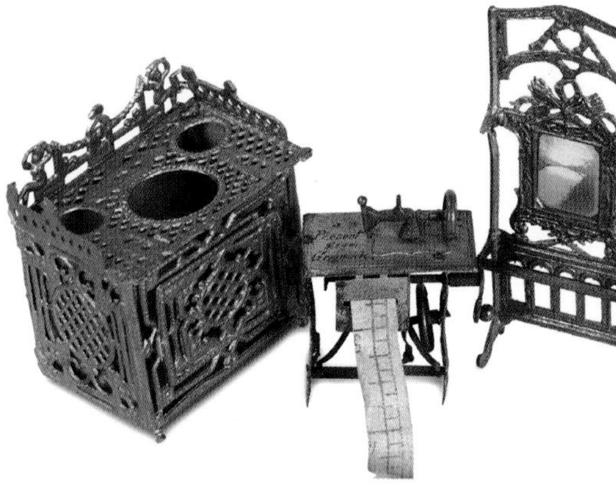

540.1. German Bisque Elevator Dollhouse, "6309", with Four Porches Attributed to Gottschalk

22"w x 25"h x 12"d. The two-story wooden framed dollhouse features a flat-topp roof with red shingles, wide dormer at the attic lever with three windows, wide chimney, original cream painted finish with green trim, featuring a set-back front door beneath a generous porch whose roof serves as a wide balcony for the front second floor. There are two doors at the front, and two on the sides, each with Gottshalk window panes and Gottschalk door handles. There are four windows each on front first and second floors, and at the sides there are porches on both floors with three steps leading to the first floor porch. The interior features two full rooms and two foyer room. The first floor foyer features a corner closet and an elevator shaft that extends to the second floor and operates from winding handle at the exterior of the house. There are two interior doors, original electrical fixtures, original wall and floor papers, and the house is furnished with wooden coat tree, hall mirror, soft metal fancy washstand, soft metal sewing machine that is actually a tape measure, soft metal firescreen with mirror, birdcage, white tin fireplace, 5 various tables and chairs and three small dolls. The house is pencil numbered "6309" on the underside. Excellent condition. Attributed to Gottschalk, circa 1912. $4000/5000

Session Two continues in Volume Two